EVOLUTION IN A NEW LIGHT

By the same author

THE SEVEN DEADLY FALLACIES

EVOLUTION IN A NEW LIGHT

THE OUTWORKINGS OF COSMIC IMAGINISM

A critical re-appraisal of evolutionary theory
offering a unique resolution of the long-standing
conflict between Evolutionism and Creationism.
Neo-Darwinism updated

ROBERT J. GILSON
CEng., MIMechE.

PELEGRIN TRUST
in association with
PILGRIM BOOKS
TASBURGH · NORWICH · ENGLAND

British Library Cataloguing-in-Publication Data

A catalogue record for this book
is available from The British Library
ISBN 0 946259 40 2

Photoset by Waveney Typesetters, Norwich
and printed in Great Britain at the University Press, Cambridge

Dedicated to

All seekers after truth

CONTENTS

ILLUSTRATIONS

PREFACE

As everybody knows, Darwin's famous Theory of Evolution, based on what he called the natural selection of random variations, first saw the light of day in the last century. In its time, the theory of natural selection seemed adequate to explain what was then known of the infinite variety of the phenomena of life, without the need to assume the intervention of a great Creator. The theory instantly endeared itself to those who did not take kindly to the Church's influence in discouraging freedom of thought, and were no longer prepared to accept without question the authoritarian doctrines of institutionalised religion. The theory quickly achieved scientific respectability, and became recognised as an authentic branch of science.

Since Darwin's day there has been an explosive expansion of knowledge in the life sciences, including biology, palaeontology, physiology, and neurology, which has brought to light much that falls outside the scope of his Theory of Evolution. But evolutionists seem to have become so preoccupied with assimilating, amplifying, refining and deploying this great flood of ever-growing knowledge, as to be in danger of losing sight of some fundamental weaknesses of the theory that are being brought to light. One example (which I deal with fully in the text) is the widespread rejection by biologists of the argument that Darwinism is a matter of chance, because, they say, the primary feature of evolution is natural selection, and this is far from being random because it is aimed at survival. The fact is, the *variations* acted upon by natural selection are, acccording to biologists themselves, purely fortuitous in respect of the needs of the organism, and it is on this basis that Darwinism can legitimately be described as chance.

It was not Darwin's intention to promote an atheistic view of life, but his followers seem to have adopted that view, enthusiastically proclaiming that the theory of evolution has removed the idea of Creation from the realm of rational discussion. A large proportion of the general public seems to have been influenced in this direction by long-continued exposure to the tenets of Darwinism and Neo-Darwinism (its modern version). However, many of them are coming to feel that a purely materialistic philosophy of life, based only upon the physical world of sensory perception and without regard for spiritual aspects, is incomplete and unsatisfying. It is to these people, who feel the need for a rational middle-way between the extremes of uncompromising materialism on the one hand, and unquestioning acceptance of ecclesiastical authority on the other hand, that this book is particularly addressed.

Many evolutionists and religionists appear to regard religion and evolution as mutually exclusive, either religion-and-God, or evolution-and-no-God. Their choice becomes a matter of personal predilection rather than reasoned logic and probability. A choice made on such a basis usually becomes quite impervious to logical arguments based on reasoning. To say the least, this seems a poor way to arrive at truth. It seems to me that a better approach would be a secular one unbiased by orthodox doctrine and dogma, whether religious or scientific, but perfectly willing to consider all aspects of the issues. Hence this book.

Whilst it is a purely secular book owing allegiance to no Church or creed, it is nevertheless compatible with the broad principle of religion in the sense of belief in a transcendental Source. As such I hope it will offend nobody, and perhaps help many. I have spared no effort to present my points clearly and succinctly, avoiding the verbiage which too often detracts from the force of an argument.

I ought to explain how it was that I came to get involved in the problems of evolution, after a lifetime spent in coping with the problems of my own profession of mechanical engineering. The whole thing was sparked off by reading, at the instigation of a friend, one of the most recent and most outspoken books written in defence of Darwinism, Richard Dawkins' strongly partisan *The Blind Watchmaker*. Apart from an instinctive distrust of the efficacy of chance in the workings of nature, I had not until then felt any compelling need to make a deep study of evolutionary theory.

But the more I pondered over what Dawkins was saying, the more perplexed I found myself. His book seemed to me to contain many fallacies and misconceptions, and in the end I decided to write to Dr Dawkins in an effort to resolve the difficulties I was experiencing. Much to my disappointment I found him unable or unwilling to help, and seemingly incapable of really understanding my problems. One thing led to another, and I found myself getting deeply involved in a study of evolutionary theory. To cut a long story short, I finished up by writing my own book, and here it is! It seems only fair to add that I offered Dr Dawkins the opportunity of reading and commenting on my book prior to its publication, but he declined the invitation.

However, I have certainly profited from a study of Dawkins' book and his brief replies to my letters, and must express my gratitude for his catalytic role in awakening my interest in the many interesting problems inhering in Darwinian evolutionary theory. Without this invaluable stimulation, this book would be in all probability never have seen the light of day. Others to whom I owe thanks for helping to mould my ideas (in the main by disagreeing with them!) are Prof. P. H. Clarke FRS, Prof. Douglas Spanner, Prof. Brian Goodwin, Sir John Eccles, John Maddox, Mark Ridley, plus a dozen thoughtful readers of the journal *Biology* who wrote to me privately to express their support of a somewhat critical article of mine that the editor had, rather surprisingly, agreed to publish.

Speaking as an engineer accustomed to coping with the practical problems of every day, I think I can offer my readers an entertaining glimpse into a very different world. It is a fantasy world of unverifiable theory and hypothesis, of uncorroborated conjecture and supposition masquerading as established fact; of slapdash reasoning and dubious argument, of partisanship and dogma. This is to name *some* of the unexpected characteristics I have run into in my survey of the territory.

Finally, I show below, for the benefit of non-mathematical readers, the meaning of the arithmetical terms I use:

billion	1,000,000,000	10^9
'rillion	1,000,000,000,000	10^{12}
quadrillion	1,000,000,000,000,000	10^{15}
quintillion	1,000,000,000,000,000,000	10^{18}
sextillion	1,000,000,000,000,000,000,000	10^{21}
septillion	1,000,000,000,000,000,000,000,000	10^{24}

Robert J. Gilson

PROLOGUE

The momentous influence of Darwinism. Willed design or unwilled evolution. Evolution and education. Moral implications. Russell's unyielding despair. Facing facts. A glossary for the uninitiated.

If it were possible to condense into a single sentence the essence of Darwinism, I suppose it might be done very simply by saying 'everything in nature evolved by the natural selection of random variations'. A rider could be added explaining that in this context *natural* means automatic or unwilled, in contrast to artificial selection practised by breeders of domesticated plants and animals; and *random* means fortuitous relative to the needs and survival of the organism or phenomenon concerned.

It would be difficult to exaggerate the influence of Darwin's evolutionary theory on the development of Western thought in this century. As D. R. Holdroyd concludes in his scholarly work *Darwinian Impacts*, 'The Darwinian revolution was unquestionably an episode of quite outstanding importance in the history of Western culture'.[39] Holdroyd outlines the impact of Darwinism in the varied fields of politics, theology, philosophy, psychology, anthropology, literature, music, and of these, I think there can be little doubt that theology has been the most deeply affected. In replacing the theological concept of a creative source by the materialistic concept of evolution based on random variations, Darwinism has been a

1

major factor in the decline of religious faith. Evolutionists insist that their theory has removed the need for the hypothesis of a creative source,[65] and this iconoclastic view has quickly permeated throughout society. Sir Julian Huxley stated on television in 1959 'Darwinism removed the whole idea of God as the Creator of organisms, from the sphere of rational discussion'. It is only fair to add that this was not Darwin's intention, but was superimposed by his disciples and followers.

However difficult it may be for modern scientifically-oriented man to accept the authoritarian doctrines of institutionalised religion, most people, I think, would agree that in an earlier era the churches did in fact exert a useful restraining influence on socially undesirable personal behaviour – an influence which is sadly lacking in the contemporary worldview based on scientific materialism. Many in the present age have come to see the role of arbiter of truth as having passed from religion to science; they can see clearly that science has made, and continues to make, great strides in their lifetime, while religion as represented by the churches seems to be concerned mainly with preserving the *status quo* of centuries-old dogma and ritual. This decline in religious influence is undoubtedly a major factor in the growth of criminality in our times. Sir John Eccles has summed it up succinctly:[23]

> Value systems that have been built up over hundreds of years are now deteriorating so that society is threatened by newly developing barbarism. Crime of all kinds ... is increasing at a menacing rate. The prison population is growing as never before. While there is so much public interest in the prevention of nuclear war with its threatened destruction of society from without, there is lamentably little interest in the destruction of society from within by the failure of our system of values.

A decisive factor in spreading the gospel of evolution throughout society has of course been our education system. Most students and graduates – certainly all those whose curriculum included biology – commence adult life thoroughly indoctrinated in the belief that evolutionary theory is an authentic part of modern science, while what little religious instruction they may have received was based on unquestioning faith rather than reasoned logic. As Rifkin has said in a fascinating book,[75] evolutionary theory has been enshrined as the centre-piece of our educational system, with elaborate walls erected to shield it from disruptive influences which could undermine the entire educational foundation of the modern worldview. Biolgist Garrett Hardin has said that if a member of the academic establishment dares to question Darwinism his sanity is immediately called into question.[75Q] The prestigious scientific journal *Nature* – 'the unofficial journal of the Scientific Establishment' – has opined, 'Nobody in their senses can deny that the doctrine of evolution is an exceedingly powerful means of relating such a variety of phenomena that it deserves to be called the truth . . . Darwin occupies a place in science at least as strong as Newton's laws'.[63] The late Professor C. H. Waddington stated 'Neo-Darwinism has become an established orthodoxy, any criticism of which is regarded as little less than *lèse-majesté* [high treason]'.[64]

Little does the earnest student of evolution realise that the tenets of evolution are just as much a matter of faith as are the tenets of religion. The doctrine of random variation is just as unprovable as is the doctrine of the Virgin Birth, and just as sacrosanct to its adherents. All we actually *know* about genetic mutations (which are usually regarded as the main cause of biological variations) is that they can be caused by physical factors such as radiation or certain chemical agents, and biologists have taken it for granted that *all* mutations are necessarily caused by these physical agents. There is absolutely no shred of evidence to support this crucial assumption, yet it seems to be regarded as established fact. One biologist has admitted 'the concept of organic evolution is very highly prized by biologists, for many of whom it is the object of genuinely religious devotion'.[13] And Dr Colin Patterson has said 'Just as pre-Darwinian biology was carried out by people whose faith was in the Creator and His plan, post-Darwinian biology is being carried out by people whose faith is in, almost, the deity of Darwin'.[51] (If this sounds a little sacriligious to anyone, they can paraphrase it to 'Just as pre-Darwinian biology was carried out by people whose faith was in the

Scriptures, post-Darwinian biology is being carried out by people whose faith is the written word of Darwin'.)

This random variation doctrine is far from being the only unproven assumption incorporated in Neo-Darwinism, and I will come to the others in due course. Suffice it to say here that after much studying and thinking about evolutionary theory, I have found myself forced to the surprising conclusion that the arguments against orthodox evolutionary theory are *at least* as weighty as those for it. Bold words maybe, but bear with me, and I think you will find them justified. I think it probable that any unbiased person (if such there be!) who carefully studied the books for and against, such as Dawkins' *The Blind Watchmaker* and Wesson's *Beyond Natural Selection*,[105] would find him or herself arriving at the same conclusion.

On this basis it seems fair to say that we have for generations been educating our young in the sadly mistaken belief that life is a meaningless accidental outcome of chance, and that the concept of a guiding intelligence is out-dated. Thus we have unwittingly encouraged the erosion of moral values referred to by Sir John Eccles in the passage quoted above. We have fostered the negative worldview epitomised by Bertrand Russell in his famous (or infamous) 'unyielding despair' peroration:[78]

> That man is the product of causes which had no prevision of the end they were achieving; that his origin, his hopes and fears, his loves and beliefs, are but the outcome of accidental collocations of atoms; that no fire, no heroism, no intensity of thought and feeling, can preserve an individual life beyond the grave; that all the labours of the ages, all the devotion, all the noonday brightness of human genius, are doomed to extinction in the vast death of the solar system, and that the whole temple of man's achievements must inevitably be buried beneath the debris of a universe in ruins – all these things, if not quite beyond dispute, are yet so nearly certain that no philosophy which rejects them can hope to stand. Only on the firm foundation of unyielding despair, can the soul's habitation be safely built.

I am all for facing the facts, but in so vital an issue let us first be

4

sure that they really *are* facts. I present in the following pages some powerful evidence suggesting that both Darwin and Russell were seriously at fault in their interpretation of the evidence, and that an uncritical public were too easily beguiled by their utterances.

Before closing this brief prelude, it will be helpful to those who find themselves intrigued by what I have said, but are doubtful of their competence to judge the issues, because of lack of familiarity with the technicalities of the subject, if I add a short explanatory glossary of technical terms together with a biographical outline of the dramatis personae involved, so here goes. . .

A Glossary for the Uninitiated

Darwinism and Neo-Darwinism

Almost everyone will have heard of Darwin's famous Theory of Evolution, but not everyone realises what a simple and indeed obvious theory it is. In essence it simply says that life in all its variety evolved from simpler beginnings by automatically adopting any small variations of structure which happened to benefit the organism in which they occurred. No two members of a family are ever identical, not even so-called identical twins, and Darwin reasoned that any of the naturally-occurring differences, which happened to confer survival advantages in the universal struggle for existence and reproduction, would be favoured by nature, and inherited by succeeding generations. Conversely any that were disadvantageous would be discarded and allowed to die out. He named this automatic acceptance of useful variations and rejection of harmful ones, *Natural Selection*, seeing it as nature's equivalent of the deliberate selection of desired characteristics by plant and animal breeders.

In some ways this naming was misleading, inasmuch as selection in this context is *not* a deliberate purposive activity by an independent autonomous agency. It is merely a passive, automatic outcome of the universal struggle to survive and reproduce.

Darwin became so enamoured of his theory that he carried it to the point of implying that the long-continued operation of natural selection over millions of years could eventuate in the transformation of one species into a different species incapable of interbreeding with the original one. This speculative implication has never been positively vindicated, despite the efforts of generations of biologists. The most that can be claimed to be established beyond reasonable doubt or argument is the evolution of advantageous new features; an event known to biologists as *adaptation*, meaning simply adaptation to changing circumstances and environments.

Charles Darwin (1809–1882) published his *magnum opus The Origin of Species by Means of Natural Selection* in 1859, under pressure from Wallace, q.v. Later he followed this with *The Variation of Animals and Plants Under Domestication* (1868), and then *The Descent of Man* (1871).

Some may wonder about the difference between Darwinism and Neo-Darwinism. The short answer is, there is no essential difference. Neo-Darwinism is simply an expanded form of Darwinism including what might be called Mendelism. Gregor Mendel was an Austrian monk who experimented with the hybridisation of plants, and in the process discovered the basic mechanisms of heredity. His book *Experiments With Plant Hybrids* was published in 1865, six years after Darwin's *Origin* appeared, but made little impression at the time, and did not become widely known until 1900, eighteen years after Darwin's death. Darwin had no solid knowledge of the actual *causes* of the slight variations occurring between individual members of a family. He could only assume that they were fortuitous variations arising from the inevitable slight imperfections in nature's reproductive processes. Mendel's work opened up the way to an understanding of the genetic system based on the DNA code. Eventually this was combined with Darwin's ideas to become what is now called Neo-Darwinism.

A. R. Wallace (1823–1913)

Alfred Russell Wallace formulated a virtually identical theory of evolution based on the natural selection of advantageous variations, concurrently with, but quite independently of, Charles Darwin. In 1858 he sent Darwin an essay written while recovering from fever in the Mollucan islands between Borneo and New Guinea, on 'the tendency of varieties to depart indefinitely from the original type'. Darwin was taken aback to find that it virtually duplicated his own ideas. He was naturally concerned at the possibility of being beaten to the post by Wallace, and the upshot was an arrangement to present both Wallace's paper and one of Darwin's at a meeting of the influential Linnean Society. However, this aroused little interest at the time, and it was not until publication of Darwin's *The Origin of Species* the following year that controversy really boiled up, fuelled by the trading of schoolboy insults between Thomas Henry Huxley, an ardent supporter of Darwin, later to become known as 'Darwin's Bulldog', and Samuel Wilberforce, the Bishop of Oxford. Bishop Wilberforce enquired of Huxley whether it was through his grandfather or his grandmother that he claimed descent from a monkey. To this Huxley replied grandly that if he had to make a choice between a poor ape for an ancestor or a man who used his gifts to ridicule scientific discussion and discredit a humble seeker after truth, he would prefer the ape. This sort of emotional atmosphere of schoolboy taunts continues to the present day in some of the discussions between the contestants in the continuing controversy between evolutionists and creationists, as can be seen from a perusal of books such as Montagu[59] and Watson.[95]

In later years Darwin and Wallace came to disagree strongly on one aspect of evolution, namely the question of whether subjective qualities such as aesthetic sense, musical and mathematical ability, and abstract thought generally, could have evolved by the natural selection of biological variations. Darwin argued that they could, taking the La Mettrie view that the brain secretes thought as the liver secretes bile. Wallace was equally strongly convinced that these sorts of intellectual and emotional qualities could not have evolved by the physical processes that brought about the evolution of biological features. This issue continues to be the subject of recrimination between evolutionists and creationists to the present day.

Mutations
The word mutation, from the Latin verb *mutare*, to change, was

originally applied to fortuitous rearrangements or copying mishaps in the genetic system. Nowadays it has become more loosely used to cover any small random changes of structure which are assumed to be caused by genetic changes. Following Darwin's lead, most biologists take it for granted that mutations are necessarily always fortuitous or random in respect of the welfare and survival of the organism in which they occur. It is relevant to add that there is, and can be, no actual *evidence* in support of this universal assumption. The mere fact that science has no knowledge of a guiding agency influencing the occurrence and nature of mutations does not prove its non-existence, any more than the fact that science has no knowledge of God proves His non-existence.

As would be expected of any complex organism, mutations are normally deleterious to its functioning, just as random changes to a machine would be. If you made random changes to a sewing machine or a car engine, you could hardly expect its performance to be improved, however long you persevered! In fact the longer you continued, the more certain you could be of detriment or total breakdown.

Life Fields

As mentioned under mutations above, most biologists take it for granted that the small structural differences which distinguish one member of a family from another, are the outcome of random mutations in the genes. But genes do not contain instructions for building bodies, they contain instructions only for building protein molecules, and we still have no real knowledge of how molecules are built into bodies. As we all do know, however, it is a fact that sexually-reproduced life passes through the stages of fertilised egg – embryo – foetus – new-born infant – child – adult. The big problem is, how does the embryo grow into the later stages? Each of the repeatedly dividing cells in the growing embryo contains a complete set of all the genes present in the adult organism, so it seems there must be something additional to the genes to guide the sequential growth and development of the embryo into a body. Some scientists have postulated that this something additional to genes is a sort of

8

'field of influence', analogous perhaps to a magnetic field. This could act as an immaterial template or mould guiding the sequential development of the embryo into a complete organism. Such fields are often called morphogenetic fields, meaning form-controlling.

Genetic System
Everybody must have heard of genes, but not everybody has a clear idea of what they are. In the nucleus of the cells of which the body is built, there are tiny thread-like components called chromosomes, and genes are sections of the chromosome consisting of closely coiled twin strands of the DNA molecule (deoxyribonucleic acid). Each of the thousands of billions of cells in the human body contains forty-six chromosomes arranged in twenty-three pairs, and the total length of the coiled strands of DNA in the cell is something like 100,000 times the width of the cell. Each cell holds a complete set of all the chromosomes and genes required to build the body proteins. When each cell divides into two new ones, the twin strands of DNA first separate into two single strands which migrate to opposite sides of the cell, where they gather materials to assemble into a new strand of DNA replacing the discarded half strand. Thus the two new cells are each provided with the full complement of forty-six chromosomes and their genes.

The germ cells or gametes, i.e., the ova and spermatozoa, each contain only a single set of the chromosomes, giving them twenty-three instead of the full forty-six of the normal cell, so that when they unite in fertilisation, the combined cell (called the zygote) is supplied with the full complement of forty-six, twenty-three from the father and twenty-three from the mother.

The DNA strands are based on four chemical 'letters', designated A – T and C – G. These four letters are the basis of the DNA code which provides the information required to build the molecules of which the body is composed. A gene may contain many thousands of the code letters arranged in a specific sequence which determines the message it carries, just as the sequence of letters in a sentence determines its meaning.

It is difficult to grasp the astonishing degree of ultra-miniaturisation

9

achieved by the genetic system. The cells of the body are so tiny that some thirty of them could fit side by side into a single human hair, and there are nearly a million billion in the human body. The nucleus of the cell, which houses the chromosomes and genes, takes up much less than a tenth of the volume of the cell, yet the total length of the DNA strands in the nucleus amounts to two metres, containing 30,000 genes each having thousands of code letters. The sequence of these letters provides the information for producing the 30,000 proteins and enzymes of the human body, such as collagen, adrenalin, insulin, keratin, actin, myosin, etc.

Chemical Bias

This term describes the fact that some of the building blocks of life, the biological monomers of which polymers such as proteins and enzymes are made, will combine only with certain favoured partners. For instance, adenine, one of the bases or 'code letters' of DNA will link only with thymine, and the base cytosine links only with guanine. It is due to this happy circumstance that a single strand of DNA is able to assemble a complementary strand to replace one discarded in the processes of cell division.

So the spontaneous combination of monomers to form polymers is not always entirely arbitrary and unrestricted, it sometimes has to follow certain favoured lines. This is sometimes seen as supporting the principle of evolution, but it is not a valid argument. There is no logical *a priori* reason why chemical bias should be advantageous to life, it could equally well be disadvantageous. For instance, if the twenty amino acids of which proteins and enzymes are made, were biased in favour of only one or two partners, this would severely restrict the number of usable combinations, and prevent the production of most of the millions of different proteins to be found in nature, thus making life as we know it, quite impossible.

Spontaneous Generation

Prior to the 17th century it was generally believed that life could and did arise spontaneously from dead matter, as for example maggots from rotting meat, flies from decaying vegetable matter, and so on.

10

This belief was held by such eminent figures as Plato, Newton, Galileo and Bacon. This changed in 1660 when the Italian physician, Francesco Redi, showed that maggots did not arise if meat was kept covered with fine gauze to keep flies off. Further work was done by Spallanzani in 1780, and by Virchow in 1858, who showed that new cells never arose except from pre-existent cells. All this work culminated in Pasteur's experiments in 1860, which proved quite conclusively that life could not arise from dead matter or inert material if it was sterilised and preserved from atmospheric contamination in sealed sterile containers.

The name of Pasteur has been immortalised in the universal process of pasteurising cow's milk; and the enormous canning industry bears witness to the validity of his findings, as also do the untold millions of tubes of bacterial culture media used all over the world in bacteriological research.

The antithesis of spontaneous generation is *biogenesis*, the principle that life can arise only from pre-existent life.

Extinction and Speciation
Extinction is the dying-out and eventual disappearance of existing species. Speciation is the process by which existing species are presumed to become transformed into new species by the long-continued cumulative action of natural selection on random variations.

Radiometric Dating
The atoms of some of the chemical elements comprising the physical world are unstable, being subject to decay or breakdown by the spontaneous radioactive emission of one of their nuclear particles. Science has been able to determine the rate at which these changes occur with a high degree of accuracy, and it is usually expressed as the 'half life', meaning the time required for half the atoms in a given material to make the change. By measuring the extent of radioactive change in a sample of current material, it is easy to estimate the age of the sample with reasonable assurance.

This estimate is based on the assumption that the rate of decay has remained constant throughout the length of time that has elapsed since the material came into existence. This assumption has been the subject of passionate controversy between evolutionists and creationists, inasmuch as *radiometric dating* as it is called, gives estimates for the age of the earth of several billions of years. In sharp contrast, the age obtained by a literalistic interpretation of the Book of Genesis is only a few thousand years. Small wonder that a discrepancy of a million to one arouses controversy!

Homo Sapiens
The Latin name for the human species. Self-christened 'man the wise'!

Perpetual Motion
Until well into the 19th century, amateur inventors were obsessed with the problem of devising a machine which would run for ever under its own steam, so to speak. Many ingenious devices were proposed, but none ever ran except under conditions of fraud! But hope springs eternal, and the thought of free power for ever, motivated people who refused to give up the dream. In 1775, the French Academy of Science resolved to no longer entertain any schemes for perpetual motion, as it came to be called, and by the early 19th century it became generally accepted that perpetual motion was a practical impossibility. The reason was, of course, quite simple once seen – movement always involves friction of one sort or another, and unless the energy absorbed in overcoming frictional resistance is supplied by an external source, any machine left to its own devices will inevitably slow down and come to a standstill.

The Big Bang
Cosmologists find that the universe is expanding in all directions, which implies that it was smaller in the past. The rate of expansion has been determined with a reasonable degree of accuracy, and is found to be directly proportional to the distance of the galaxies, which suggests that it all started as an explosion, in which the debris that travels farthest must have moved the fastest.

It has been calculated that the universe must have been in an unimaginably compressed condition some ten to fifteen billion years ago, prior to which neither space nor time existed, or so the scientists tell us. At time zero the 'primordial egg' of virtually *infinite* density and temperature exploded in an inconceivably violent *Big Bang* of radiant energy far too hot to condense into atoms of matter. This primordial fireball expanded very rapidly, and after a million years had grown to billions of billions of kilometres in size, and cooled sufficiently to allow the formation of a white-hot cloud of hydrogen and helium atoms. In the succeeding hundreds of millions of years this vast expanding cloud of gas condensed into the untold trillions of stars which make up the present-day universe, just as a cloud of steam condenses into water molecules as it cools.

Energy
Energy is the stuff of which the world is made. The great Werner Heisenberg, one of the principal founding fathers of modern physics, stated firmly 'Energy is the fundamental stuff of which the world is made. . . . The elementary particles [of which atoms are made] are the form which energy must take in order to become matter'. Albert Einstein, inventor of Relativity Theory, has shown that energy and matter are interchangeable; energy can be converted into matter, and matter into energy, as witness the nuclear power industry and atomic armaments. Energy is everywhere and in everything. In a very real sense, energy is all there is.

Energy can take many forms, for example atomic energy, chemical, electrical, mechanical, hydraulic, pneumatic energy. It exists in two stages, locked-in potential energy, and free or usable energy. It is defined as the capacity to perform work or provide power, but that describes its potential or capability, not its inward nature. Nobody knows what its essential nature or make-up *is*. All science can tell us is that it is eternal, indestructible, inexhaustible. Einstein is reputed to have observed that it can be likened to thought waves of the Central Mind, which is the nucleus of *all* energy. This nucleus cannot be described or defined; the concentration of energy is so incredibly intense that it defies description even in scientific terms. A distinguished contemporary physicist, David Bohm, postulates that the apparently empty vacuum of space, far from being empty, is in fact a plenum or reservoir of enormous quantities of locked-in 'zero point' energy, far exceeding in amount the total mass-energy of the universe. One way or the other, it seems not unreasonable to regard energy as an emanation, or outflowing, or essence, of the Cosmic Intelligence, call it God or Allah or Brahma; whatever your personal background favours.

Monism, Dualism, Reductionism, Materialism, Holism

These are philosophical terms which for practical everyday purposes can be interpreted as follows: *Monism* is the doctrine that matter is the only reality and all else, such as mind and spirit, is simply the outcome or effect of brain activity. *Dualism* is the doctrine that mind and spirit, although closely related to the brain, are independent realities in their own right. *Reductionism* is the doctrine that all the phenomena of the physical world can be reduced to and explained in terms of, the properties of its smallest parts; that thought can be reduced to brain activity, emotions and behaviour to hormones and secretions, biology to chemistry, and so on. *Materialism* is the doctrine that only matter is real, all else is illusion. *Holism* is the doctrine that everything, mind *and* body, spirit *and* matter or energy, is a single unitary whole, undivided, not separated.

It will be seen that Monism, Reductionism, and Materialism amount to much the same thing, with Dualism as their antithesis, and Holism amounting to a higher version of Dualism, so to speak.

Helen Keller (1880–1968)

Helen Keller was stricken with complete blindness and deafness at the tender age of twenty months, when she had only a few words of baby talk which were quickly lost in the silent world of darkness. Although tenderly cared for by her family, she seemed to have little prospect of attaining anything approaching normality as an adult, with her tragic restriction of sensory input to touch, taste and smell. She was a high-spirited but uncontrolled child. When she was almost seven years of age, Anne Sullivan joined her, to undertake the daunting task of her education. Miss Sullivan first broke through Helen's isolation by pouring water on one hand, while tracing the letters w-a-t-e-r on the other, at first very slowly, then gradually increasing speed. This was a tremendous revelation to Helen, who quickly grasped the possibilities of language. She immediately started to learn a multitude of words and their meaning. With superb enthusiasm, intelligence and perseverance, she made remarkable progress, and became an accomplished scholar. She took an Arts degree by reading English, French and German classics in the original. Prior to her association with Anne Sullivan, her beloved 'Teacher', she was scarcely a human being, yet by the heroic efforts of them both, she became a wonderfully rich and gifted personality, able to engage in public speaking with understanding and insight. A truly inspiring story of the triumph of the human spirit over appalling adversity which would have broken anybody less courageous.

Francis Bacon (1561–1626)
Sir Francis Bacon was one of the greatest names in Renaissance philosophy. He was a warm-hearted man of many talents, wide knowledge, and high principles, who devoted his life to public service, both in political and intellectual fields. He became a barrister at the age of twenty-one, a Member of Parliament at twenty-three, Attorney General at fifty-two, and Lord Chancellor at fifty-six. In 1621 he was made Viscount St Albans.

He distrusted the 'scholastic' flavour of medieval philosophy, and favoured the empirical practical approach. He loved exactness of expression, and is widely respected for his writings. His greatest work, the *Novum Organum*, (loosely translated as 'A new principle of intellectual investigation') was published in 1620. It has been said that in him the Renaissance reached complete fruition. Some have asserted that he was the author of Shakespeare's works. Ben Jonson had a high regard for his character and abilities. Certainly he was one of the greatest men of his times.

Bertrand (Lord) Russell (1872–1970)
Bertrand William Arthur Russell, 3rd Earl, was educated at

Cambridge. He became an attaché at the British Embassy in Paris. He devoted his studies mainly to mathematics, philosophy, and education, and opened a school in Hampshire where children were given free play and encouraged to develop their individuality without restraint.

He was regarded as one of the foremost thinkers of his age, and published many essays and books, including *Philosophical Essays* (1910), *Principia Mathematica* (1911–13), *Introduction to Mathematical Philosophy* (1918), *Sceptical Essays* (1928), *Conquest of Happiness* (1930), *The Scientific Outlook* (1931), and *Education and the Social Order* (1932). Obviously he was not one to be lost for words!

He was a noted atheist who had no time whatever for religion, as can be judged from his 'unyielding despair' passage quoted on page 4. As his daughter said in her biography of him, there was somewhere at the bottom of his heart, the depths of his soul, (he would never have forgiven her for that word!) an empty space which had once been filled by God, and he never found anything else to put in it.

George Berkeley (1685–1753)
A celebrated Irish prelate and philosopher, Bishop of Cloyne from 1734 to 1752. His *Principles of Human Knowledge* was published in 1710. His philosophy was founded on the belief that only the spiritual or mental is real, as expressed in his oft-quoted words:

> All the choir of Heaven and all the furniture of earth, in a word all those bodies which comprise the mighty frame of the world, have not any existence without a mind . . . So long as they are not perceived by me or do not exist in my mind or that of any other created spirit, they must either have no existence at all, or else must subsist in the mind of some eternal spirit.

To Berkeley it was inconceivable that the mind should be able to interact with something radically different to itself. This is concordant with what the Nobel Laureate Konrad Lorenz wrote nearly 300 years later, referring to 'That most mysterious of barriers, utterly impenetrable to human understanding . . . that separates our subjective experience from the verifiable physiological events that occur in our body'.

After all, it is a fact that there are no sensory stimuli in the brain or nervous system, only electrochemical activity among the neural circuits. The physical world of 'objective' matter is simply a mental image or construct in the mind or consciousness. Berkeley was nothing if not logical!

Armed with these notes on the principal ideas and players involved, we can now proceed with the matter in hand . . .

CHAPTER ONE

A NON-PHYSICAL REALM

Assessing the credibility of a creative source. The immateriality of mind and matter. Emotions and sensations not explicable in terms of brain activity. How to believe your beliefs are not true. Physical manifestation preceded by non-physical idea. Scientists' views on religion. Success of the Monist approach.

The crucial issue at the heart of the Russell quotation on page 4 is the question of whether or not the hypothesis of a non-physical creative source is credible. Obviously we cannot *prove* the case either way, but we can at least weigh the pros and cons with an open mind. If in so doing we decide the hypothesis is *not* credible, then there are no logical grounds for rejecting the Russell view, and we may as well shut the shop and accept the doctrines of Neo-Darwinism without more ado. But if we decide to the contrary, we should examine Neo-Darwinian evolutionary theory very carefully, in view of its momentous implications.

As those readers with some background of acquaintance with science will doubtless be aware, scientists tell us that matter itself is essentially immaterial, with the subatomic 'particles' of which it is composed being nothing but condensations or coagulations of *energy*, 'regions of an energy field where the field density is enormously high'.[11] The great physicist Werner Heisenberg put it unequivocally: 'Energy is the fundamental stuff of which the world is made. . . . The elementary particles are the form which energy must take in order to become matter'.[36] Max Planck said at a lecture in Florence, 'There is no matter as such . . . All matter originates and exists only by virtue of a force which brings the particles of an atom into vibration and holds . . . the atom together. . . . We must assume behind this force the existence of a conscious and intelligent Mind'.[18] Quantum physics tells us that consciousness or mind is an integral factor in the interactions of particle physics. And E. H. Walker has propounded a theory of elementary units, or monads, of consciousness which control the outcome of a quantum uncertainty event.[93] The distinguished contemporary physicist David Bohm has postulated an *Implicate Order* of undifferentiated primary energy in which is enfolded the explicate order of manifested physical objects and phenomena.[7]

Energy fields themselves are intangible and impalpable, detectable only by their effects, and can fairly be described as non-physical or immaterial. Science can tell us nothing about this universal energy, it can only say it is just there, inexhaustible, indestructible, everlasting. But despite the ignorance of science, this universal energy must surely have a source, an origin. Einstein is reputed to have likened it to thought waves of the Central Mind which is the nucleus of all energy. John Davidson echoes this when he says that the physical world and our minds are both a dance of energy.[18]

Consider now the human mind. Contemporary science tends to regard it as nothing but the effect or outcome of brain activity, but this view does not stand up to critical examination. Take the physical activity known as laughter – the sudden expulsions of breath and voice, the facial grimaces and bodily shaking etc. No doubt there are circuits in the motor cortex of the brain which control this strange muscular activity, but what causes the cortical activity? The obvious answer, that it is the feeling of amusement, makes sense only if the feeling of amusement is something other than the effect of brain activity, since you can hardly say that amusement is at one and the same time the cause and effect of brain activity. Nor can you evade this difficulty by arguing that different areas of the brain are involved, one for amusement, one for laughter. Brain cells are not autonomous self-activating units; their activity is initiated by an extraneous influence. In the case of sensory perception this external influence is of course the flow of incoming signals from the sensory organs. But we have no sensory organ for the perception of amusement. What amuses one person may not amuse another. So what could initiate the amusement-causing activity in its supposed area of the brain? If amusement and laughter *were* each the outcome of brain activity, which would come first, and why? It would seem just as logical to argue that laughter causes amusement, as the converse! Surely the only rational answer is that amusement is in the mind, not the brain. Immaterial mind and material brain can interact, and the mere fact that we are unable to explain how they do so,* casts no doubt on the existence of either, it simply demonstrates the limitations of human understanding.

Consider next another phenomenon, that of colour. Scientists from Newton onwards have insisted that colour is purely a mental sensation devoid of physical existence. When a partial spectrum of light impinges on the eye, electrical signals flash along the optic nerves to the brain where they set up a complex dynamic pattern of pulsing electro-chemical discharges in the neural circuitry – and lo and behold, we immediately experience the unpredictable and inexplicable sensation known as colour. There is no colour anywhere in the brain or nervous system, so how can the brain be expected to convert its physical activity into the non-physical sensation of colour? It is like expecting a radio set to convert its internal currents into music when no music is being transmitted from the radio station. Newton was right – colour is purely a mental sensation devoid of objective physical existence.

The same applies to all our sensations and emotions. Whatever we perceive through our human senses of sight, hearing, smell, taste or touch, the resulting brain activity is simply a dynamic pattern of electrochemical pulses, and the stimuli which reach the sensory organ never reach the brain cells or circuits. It can only be the *mind* which interprets the brain activity into perceptual sensation, just as it can only be the mind which is the seat of emotions.

Consider the mysterious phenomenon of pain. We all know only too well that an injury to the body causes the unpleasant sensation

---

* But see Walker and Eccles on page 101.

known as pain, and we know that nerve signals generated at the sight of the injury are transmitted to the brain. What we do not know is how this causes the sensation of pain. If it were true that consciousness is the effect of brain activity, this would mean that the neural activity was aware of itself. Does it make sense to say that any sort of electrical or chemical activity is aware of its effects? Is the current flow in the coils of a loudspeaker aware of the speech or music it generates? Surely the only sane answer is 'No, of course not'. If it *were* true that the brain is conscious of the pain signals in its circuitry, one might logically expect the pain to be felt in the brain, whereas it is of course felt at the site of the injury. Not only does the brain not feel the pain signals transmitted to it, but no pain is experienced when the site of the injury is in the brain itself. The Nobel Laureate, Konrad Lorenz, referred to 'That most mysterious of barriers, utterly impenetrable to human understanding . . . that separates our subjective experience from the verifiable physiological events that occur in our body'.[23] It seems to me that the barrier becomes a little less impenetrable when it is realised that our subjective experience is in the immaterial mind, not the material brain.

Consider one more case, that of voluntary bodily movement. We decide to raise our arm, and hey presto, our arm immediately rises. We know that the immediate cause of muscular movement is neural activity in the motor cortex in the brain, but what causes this neural activity? We can hardly say that volition is the outcome of brain activity, since this would mean that in the brain, cause and effect are the same thing. Nor can we evade the difficulty by saying that different areas of the brain are involved, one for volition, the other for motor activity, since this leaves unresolved the question of what *initiates* volition in its own part of the brain – the same problem that we ran into in the case of laughter.

The foregoing points can be indicated diagrammatically thus:

$$Amusement \longrightarrow brain \longrightarrow laughter$$
$$Volition \longrightarrow brain \longrightarrow movement$$
$$Sensation \longleftarrow brain \longleftarrow stimulus$$
$$Or\ more\ generally - Subjective \rightleftarrows brain \rightleftarrows Objective$$

21

The two-way interaction between mental and physical, or mind and body, with the brain as an intermediary, applies to a much wider field of behaviour than the few examples given here, of course. In daily life we are constantly exercising our ability to choose, to decide and initiate – whether to mow the lawn, write a letter, watch television, ponder an idea – in an endless list of activities. We take all such routine for granted, but we are exercising our volition all the time, apart from those activities that have become habitual and automatic.

A simple practical example of the operation of mind is provided by the intentionally-ambiguous drawing, such as the outlined cube that suddenly turns back to front, or the stairs that change into a ceiling

cornice. The change-over is spontaneous and abrupt, without any transitional stage. The signals sent to the eye and the brain do not change, and it can only be the perceiving mind which switches its interpretation between the two alternative representations.

The brain is a physical structure, and like any physical structure or machine or mechanism, its current condition must be affected by its past history, in a continuous chain of cause and effect. So if it were the brain that translated its own activity into sensations and perceptions, these could vary with its present condition. Colours, for instance, would depend on the brain's condition at the time they were viewed.

The postulate that the mind is the outcome of brain activity is irrational and indeed, self-contradictory. If thoughts and beliefs *were* nothing but a reflection of brain activity, then the theory that the mind is nothing but the outcome of brain activity would be 'true' only for those whose brain condition happened to favour it. Other beliefs by other brains would be just as 'true'. As the famous geneticist J. B. S. Haldane put it, 'If my mental processes are determined solely by the motions of atoms in my brain, I have no reason to believe that my beliefs are true'.[31]

Consider one more point. All man-made products originate as an *idea* in a *mind*, and are brought into physical existence by mental effort directed to designing and producing the article. Never in human history has a manufactured article originated in, or been improved by, a process of accumulating random manufacturing variations, and it seems safe to say that none ever will be. Always the material product is preceded by the immaterial idea. Is there any reason to suppose that this basic pivotal principle, of immaterial *idea* necessarily preceding physical manifestation, may not apply also to nature's products? I do not think so. Admittedly there can be no positive *proof* of the matter either way, but we can at least use our reasoning abilities to weigh up, as best we can, the practical probabilities. If after due consideration we arrive at a tentative conclusion that the postulate of a creative purposive source is a reasonable alternative to the postulate of blind purposeless chance, this may not finally decide the issue, but it does at least leave the way open for further consideration.

Summing up this brief examination of a subject which has been the disputing-ground of philosophers for millenia, it seems to me abundantly clear that there are no *a priori* logical grounds for dismissing the concept of a creative purposive source, perhaps a suprahuman *mind* which originates the ideas underlying the infinite variety of nature's products, just as our little human minds underly our manufactured products. This view is far from being unscientific; on the contrary, one of the greatest of all scientists, Albert Einstein, openly declared his acceptance of 'a religious feeling of rapturous amazement at the harmony of natural law which reveals an intelligence of such superiority that compared with it, all the systematic thinking and acting of human beings is an utterly insignificant reflection'.[24] And others of similar stature have expressed like-minded views, with names such as Bohr, De Broglie, Heisenberg, Newton, Pauli, Schrödinger, J. J. Thomson, Whitehead, and so on.[97]

I find it informative to compare Einstein's view with that of Richard Dawkins, who holds that the concept of a Creator is unacceptable because we cannot account for His existence.[19/316] Dawkins argues that if the odds against the spontaneous origin of a complex biological structure such as the eye are impossibly high, then the odds against the spontaneous origin of an omnipotent deity are still more impossible, so we may as well give up the idea and settle for the lesser impossibility! In other words, since our little human minds are unable to explain the origin and existence of a deity, we should reject the possibility. Not an argument I find convincing, nor, I suspect, would have Einstein. My money is on Einstein!

With the arguments for the existence of a non-physical or transcendental source so persuasive, I find it more than a little strange that most scientists seem to dismiss it off-hand without serious thought. It seems that they are so impressed with the results of the monist, reductionist, mechanist approach that has been found so successful in unravelling the secrets of nature, that they are suspicious of any other approach. This is perhaps understandable, and even desirable up to a point, but it involves a danger of losing sight of the *why* of things in the process of examining the *how* in ever-increasing detail. *It is questionable whether the search for truth is better served by referring everything to an all-embracing presumptive physical process based on chance, than by referring every unresolved problem to an all-embracing presumptive creative power.* After all, nobody can prove that there is not a transcendental creative power underlying the phenomena of nature.

It seems to me foolishly short-sighted to dismiss the possibility when a thoughtful analysis suggests it is a rational solution to an otherwise unresolved problem.

CHAPTER II

UNNATURAL SELECTION

The Richard Dawkins fallacies. The selecting agency. Demonstration of potency of guided mutations. Saving the infants. Non-sequential selection. Mutual amazement!

Richard Dawkins maintains that evolution is *not* a matter of chance, on the specious grounds that natural selection is the primary feature of Darwinism, and natural selection is non-random inasmuch as it selects for survival. According to Dawkins, the selecting agency is death,[19/62] but this is surely a radical misconception. All are fair prey to Death's sickle. He takes whatever comes along, young or old, weak or strong, quite indiscriminately. More often than not, death comes by sheer bad luck, perhaps by being in the wrong place at the wrong time. It seems probable that the majority of deaths in the wild are of the young, rather than the full grown vigorous adults. Darwin wrote[77]

> How will the struggle for existence . . . act in regard to variation? . . . Can it be thought improbable that variations useful in some way to each being in the great and complex battle of life, should sometimes occur in the course of thousands of generations? If such do occur, can we doubt (*remembering that many more individuals are born than can possibly survive*) that individuals having any advantage, however slight, over others, would have the best chance of surviving and procreating their kind? On the other

hand, we may feel sure that any variations in the least degree injurious would be rigidly destroyed. This preservation of favourable variations and the rejection of injurious variations, I call natural selection. [My italics].

All life struggles desperately to survive and reproduce, and if it can be said there *is* any active selecting agency at work in nature, I suggest that it can only be this imperative will to live, or the instinct of self-preservation. But an instinct common to *all* life, from the most primitive to the most sophisticated, can hardly be said to have originated in variations in any form or forms of life. When I say *all* life, some may object that it is not legitimate to talk of 'instinct' when it comes to elementary forms of life such as bacteria, or to the botanical realm, but I suggest it is a matter of degree. The will to live is at its most obvious in sentient life, but is still present, I suggest, in less sensitive forms of life. Even trees are known to develop synergetic strategies for dealing with pests and blights. So it seems that if natural selection can be seen as a process at all, it is not one which could itself have arisen by the workings of Darwinian evolutionary theory!

The variations postulated by Darwin as conferring 'any advantage however slight' would presumably tend to take the form, by and large, of improvements to features such as sensory acuity, reaction times, muscular agility and stamina, digestive flexibility, camouflage effectiveness, and so on. It is easy to understand how changes of this sort could benefit the adults of a species, but less easy to see how their young would benefit. If the most dangerous time of life is early infancy, as Darwin seems to suggest, then how could natural selection operate effectively on variations which benefit mainly the full-grown adult? It might be argued that advantage to the parent will increase the power of parental protection, but on the other hand, it seems questionable whether any such indirect advantage to the babies could outweigh any evolutionary advantages accruing to the adult *predator*. All things considered, it seems to me that the action of natural selection in nature may well be considerably less potent than evolutionists consider it to be.

To return to Dawkins, having asserted that death, 'the grim reaper', is the selecting agency, he proceeds to explain his idea of how selection actually works. He stresses the astronomical improbabilities of the spontaneous evolution of a complex structure such as the eye, in a single giant step, and postulates instead a system of *cumulative* selection in a long series of tiny intermediate steps. He demonstrates the tremendous advantage of cumulative selection by some ingenious computer exercises in which a random selection of twenty-seven characters 'evolves' into a twenty-eight character predetermined phrase, 'Methinks it is like a weasel', a line from Shakespeare. As he points out, the odds against producing this phrase by random selection of the letters of the alphabet in a single try are 27^{28} to 1, an enormous number which works out to untold trillions of trillions of trillions to 1. (A trillion is a million million, or 10^{12}.) But by programming the computer to select cumulatively, it succeeds in producing the target phrase in only a few dozen runs.

This may sound too good to be true, but it is easily explained by some simple arithmetic. To make it easy to follow, let us start with a single word instead of a phrase as used by Dawkins. Take the six-letter word 'chance'. If you aim to select at random from an alphabet of twenty-six letters, six letters arranged in the sequence C-H-A-N-C-E, the odds against success in a single try would be 26^6 to 1. (For those not familiar with mathematical notation, 26^6 simply means 26 multiplied by itself five times). This works out to 300,000,000 to 1. But if you program the computer to select the same letters in any old order, then the odds become very much more favourable. The odds for the first hit become $26/6$ to 1 (since a hit can be scored in any one of six places), for the second hit $26/5$ to 1, for the third hit $26/4$, for the fourth hit $26/3$, for the fifth hit $26/2$, and for the sixth hit $26/1$. The total odds for the complete word are obtained by adding all the individual odds, since each hit is independent, unlike the previous case where they were interdependent and therefore had to be multiplied. Thus the odds against, for the complete word, are $(26/6 + 26/5 + 26/4 + 26/3 + 26/2 + 26/1)$, which evaluates to 64 to 1. Quite an improvement on the single-shot odds of 300,000,000 to 1!

In the case of the Dawkins phrase, we have a twenty-seven

character alphabet (including one for the inter-word space) and a twenty-eight character phrase, so the odds become ($^{27}/_{28}$ + $^{27}/_{27}$ + $^{27}/_{26}$ + $^{27}/_{25}$ + ... $^{27}/_1$) to 1, which evaluates to 106 to 1. No wonder Dawkins thought he had solved the problem of the astronomical odds of single-shot selection!

According to Dawkins, the computer took only about half this number of tries, which seems a bit odd(!), although it might just have been the vagaries of chance – after all, if the 'odds against' are calculated at 106 to 1, this simply means that in repeated runs you are likely to succeed once every 106 tries, *on average*. Obviously individual runs will vary from the average, and variations of up to say 50 per cent are quite conceivable. But it seems unlikely that they would all be in the same direction, of course. And there was a further oddity in the computer results, namely that in two consecutive runs the last character was matched in only three or four tries instead of the average expectation of twenty-seven. This seems to suggest that the available pool of characters had by then fallen below the original figure of twenty-seven, possibly by withdrawing the mis-matches occurring earlier in the run. If so, this is clearly not representative of selection in nature. However, all this is mere detail which although hard to account for, does not detract from the dramatic demonstration of the vast improvement in probabilities which cumulative selection gives, compared with single-shot selection in one giant step.

However, apart from these relatively trivial details, there are some major fallacies in assuming that the type of cumulative selection demonstrated by the computer simulation is applicable to biology, fallacies of which Dawkins seems blissfully unaware. It is true that he does point out one anomaly, namely that the computer program is directed to a long-term end target, whereas natural selection is not directed and has no end target in view.[19/50] This admission rather seems to contradict the repeated assertion elsewhere in his book, that natural selection is aimed at survival and reproduction. But no matter, there are more weighty issues at stake.

For instance, the computer program seems to have been arranged to 'lock in' any lucky hits as they occurred, thus eliminating the possibility of adverse 'mutations'. This is totally at variance with the workings of nature, where harmful mutations greatly outweigh favourable ones. Dawkins admits this: 'Of all the possible changes that might occur to an existing complex [biological] organ, the vast majority will make it worse'.[19/306] It is difficult to find any numerical information about the likely proportion of favourable to adverse mutations, but Kitcher seems to suggest a figure in the region of 1 in 1000.[40] Bearing in mind that mutations are held to be purely random, without any trace of rhyme or reason, in respect of the welfare and survival of the organism involved, this figure seems very conservative. It could easily be 1 in 10,000 or 1 in 100,000, or maybe even 1 in 1,000,000. In the computer simulation, favourable 'mutations' are locked in as they occur, whereas in nature the very occasional favourable mutation providing a slight marginal advantage, can easily be suppressed or nullified by the far more numerous adverse mutations following. Dawkins himself says 'A single mutational step can easily be reversed'.[19/94] This could sometimes result in a false start; even, perhaps, a 'return to square one' situation quite late in the series.

More important still, the computer simulation program allows individual hits or 'mutations' to occur *anywhere in the series* without regard for logical sequence. This cannot be representative of the workings of biology. To draw a crude analogy, it is like trying to build a brick wall by inserting bricks into empty spaces in the future wall-to-be. In terms of embryology it is like expecting to grow a finger nail before a finger, or an nose before a face. This is ridiculous. You cannot expect a part to grow irrespective of other parts. Quite obviously an embryo has to grow in accordance with some sort of predetermined sequence. If you bring this quintessential sequence control into the computer simulation, you totally alter the results. You come right back, either partially or wholly, to the single-shot system with its astronomical odds against success, which Dawkins puts out of court as a practical possibility.

The point becomes still more obvious in the case of complex biological organs having a number of interconnected parts which need to come into existence concurrently in order to function properly. Take just one example, much used by Dawkins himself, the eye. Consider the eye-focusing mechanism, comprising a ring-muscle system surrounding the elastic lens and connected to the brain so as to respond automatically to the user's volition, or whatever you call his ability to look at either near or distant objects. When focused on a near object, the muscle contracts to deform the lens and increase its curvature. The point is – this mechanism cannot function properly until all the elements are present in the right place, and properly connected to the brain. Isolated bits of muscle or nerve would be worse than useless. You *must* have a muscle system of the right strength, sited in the right place and properly connected to the right part of the brain, and these features *must* be introduced together or at least concurrently, not piecemeal, since, as any photographer will know, a malfunctioning focusing system would be inferior to a simple fixed-focus system. The usual answer given by evolutionists to this sort of problem is that the early stages of the item in question probably served some other purpose, and only adapted to its present purpose at a later date; but it seems unlikely that an incipient eye could have served any other purpose than response to the visible frequencies of radiant energy, or in other words, light. And in any case, it is hard to understand why, even if this happened, it should have obviated the problems of sequence control.

There are many bodily items which although not interconnected to other items, cannot fulfil their function until fully grown. Consider for instance, the eyelid, with its dual function of protecting and lubricating the cornea by the automatic blink reflex, and facilitating sleep by shutting out visual signals from the external world. It seems unlikely that a partial eyelid would be of much use to its owner. How could an effective eyelid evolve by a long series of discrete unconnected mutations of the type demonstrated by Dawkins? The cumulative selection process postulated by Dawkins as the complete answer to the impossible odds against single-shot selection, would be likely to produce a misshapen eyelid growing in the wrong place and having eyelashes scattered anywhere over its surface! Yet the only flaw he finds in it, or at least the only one he mentions, is that in the computer exercise there was a long-term target, whereas nature has no such target or direction.

It would be easy to find further examples, but one more will suffice; the haemoglobin molecule, again used by Dawkins. Haemoglobin gives blood its unique ability to take up oxygen from the air in the lungs, and transport it to the muscles, where it exchanges the oxygen for carbon dioxide, the waste product from muscle activity. Surely a very remarkable achievement. Haemoglobin has fifty times the oxygen-carrying capacity of sea water from which it is said to have evolved. The molecule consists of four chains of amino acids twisted together and folded into an intricate three-dimensional knot. The point is, that when building a chain, each link has to be assembled to its immediate neighbour sequentially, in contrast to the non-sequential system postulated by Dawkins. And if, as in this case, the links *have* to run in a specific order, this requirement is further emphasised. Dawkins himself quotes the odds against assembling just one of the four chains correctly, as 10^{190} to 1, a quite impossibly vast number. How utterly impossible then for the folded four-chain molecule to arise by Dawkins' cumulative selection system! Yet he writes 'It is amazing that you can still read calculations like [this] haemoglobin calculation . . . as though they constituted arguments against Darwin's theory'.[19/49] Amazement seems the apt word, but in the reverse direction!

Leaving amazement at this misconception aside, it occurs to me that the Dawkins' computer demonstration makes sense if looked at from a different angle. Natural selection is, by definition, a matter of selecting from a very large number of random mutations, only those rare few which happen to be beneficial to the organism concerned. In the computer demonstration there are virtually *no* harmful mutations, hence there is nothing for selection to do. What Dawkins has actually demonstrated, and demonstrated quite unequivocally if unintentionally, is *the power of an underlying guiding intelligence to control the outcome of mutations.* This revised view of the demonstration retains the advantage of beating the problem posed with single-shot random selection and its impossibly high odds against success, which was what Dawkins was really seeking. He seems to have found an intelligible answer quite accidentally.

APPENDIX

Calculation of the odds for phrase-building exercises of the Dawkins type, becomes very laborious for those without a computer at their disposal, particularly with characters running into double figures, and the graph on page 33 (Figure 1) will be useful for those wishing to evaluate their own examples.

It is interesting to note that for values of N over 4, P can be calculated with adequate accuracy from the empirical formula

$$P = A (2.3 \mathrm{Log} N + .6)$$

where A = number of characters in alphabet, and

N = number of characters in phrase.

P = Chances to one against.

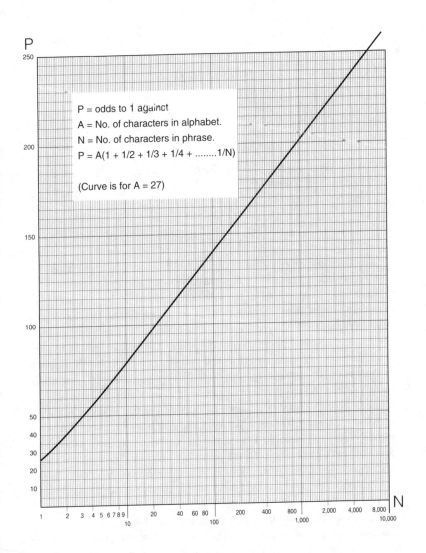

P = odds to 1 against
A = No. of characters in alphabet.
N = No. of characters in phrase.
$P = A(1 + 1/2 + 1/3 + 1/4 + \ldots\ldots1/N)$

(Curve is for A = 27)

Figure 1

CHAPTER III

MORE UNNATURAL SELECTION

Computerised doodles. Francis Bacon's explanation. The brain-eye complex. Non-sequential evolution? Anything evolves from anything?

In an attempt to overcome the self-admitted objection that his computerised, phrase-building exercise was not representative of natural selection because it was directed to a long-term goal, Dawkins sought another exercise that would eliminate this flaw. The new exercise took the form of a computer tree-graphics program designed to 'evolve' plane shapes by using changeable 'genes' to vary such factors as line length and angle, vertical or horizontal compression or expansion, depth of repetition, etc. By 'breeding' from visually selected intermediate stages in a run, he was able to cause a great variety of shapes to appear on the screen, many of which could, with the aid of a lively imagination, be likened to such a miscellany of objects as – aircraft, candelabra, bat, laboratory balance, cat's cradle, clown standing on head, ballet dancers, frog, fox, insect, kangaroo, lunar lander, man in a cocked hat, table lamp, church window, and so on. Quite a hodgepodge indeed – you name it, you can find it.

Dr Dawkins provides an interesting account of his emotional reaction to the unexpected appearance of these shapes on his computer screen: 'As I first watched these exquisite creatures emerging before my eyes, I distinctly heard the triumphal opening

34

of chords of the *2001* theme music in my mind. I couldn't eat, and that night my insects swarmed behind my eyelids as I tried to sleep'.[19/60] I don't wish to seem unkind, but perhaps I may be excused for suggesting that this is a somewhat intemperate reaction to the outcome of a computer game?

Dawkins christened his computer-generated shapes 'Biomorphs', although anything more remote from biology or morphology would be hard to devise. Indeed, I find them even less relevant than the preceding phrase-building exercise. As Prof. Brian Goodwin of The Open University has pointed out, genes do not generate shapes, nor do they contain instructions for building organisms. As he puts it, instructions for building organisms are no more encoded in DNA molecules than instructions for building snow flakes are encoded in H_2O molecules.[29]

Dawkins claims that this exercise is much more realistic than the earlier phrase-building one, although as he admits, it is still deficient, in that it uses deliberate choice instead of automatic selection. He speaks of it as generating 'an almost endless variety of quasi-biological forms'.[19/60] But surely it is stretching analogy to unreasonable lengths to equate computer-graphics with biological forms. As anyone who examines the illustrations in *The Blind Watchmaker* will find, the alleged likenesses are fanciful, to say the least. If they can be regarded as realistic at all, it is mainly to inanimate objects rather than life forms. I append overleaf a rough sketch of Dawkins' 'insects', shown in his book, Figure 4, as 'evolving' from a simple dot in twenty-nine easy stages. This is the 'exquisite creature which emerged to the sound of trumpets'. Yet the figure does not look all that convincing as a caricature of an insect. It could equally well be seen as a pair of crossed spears, or a cooking trestle, an ornamental hat-and-coat stand, or maybe an emaciated ballet-dancer. Are not these computer-generated shapes mere glorified doodles? Almost the only thing they can be said to demonstrate is that an accumulation of small changes of detail can eventuate in a large overall change.

There are two points which seem to have escaped Dawkins. Firstly, the program did not cater for adverse mutations, so that, as

35

Figure 2

in the case of the phrase-building exercise, there was nothing for selection to *do*, no mixed bag of good and bad mutations from which to select. The other point was that the exercise provided a dramatic example of the need for mutations to follow a definite sequence if they are to eventuate in a desired result; thus Dawkins found it very difficult to duplicate the original 'insects' which emerged unexpectedly and were then lost because he had not kept a record of the precise sequence of 'mutations' which had produced them. Even this practical experience was not enough to awaken him to the absence of sequential control in the phrase-building demonstration. It seems that the only useful thing the Dawkins' doodles demonstrate is the over-riding power of will or whim to decide the outcome of *sequential* cumulative mutations.

When I first noticed these unexpected flaws in the case presented by Richard Dawkins I began to think that perhaps my admittedly amateur approach, and lack of expert knowledge of the subject matter, was causing me to be unaware of some factors which would explain and vindicate Dawkins' arguments. I therefore decided to obtain and study some of the press reviews of *The Blind Watchmaker* before going any further. Much to my surprise, however, I could find no mention of these flaws in the reviews I saw; it seemed that the reviewers had simply swallowed them whole. For instance, an eminent American philosopher of science, Prof. Philip Kitcher, in a review in the prestigious journal *Nature*,[66] wrote enthusiastically of 'passages of exposition that deserved sustained applause', when referring to the 'ingenious and illuminating' demonstrations of the effectiveness of cumulative selection. He was so impressed that he went on to suggest that the Dawkins' programs should be made widely available, particularly to school children and 'eminent astrophysicists', an obvious dig at Sir Fred Hoyle who has expressed doubts about evolutionary theory. Another American philosopher of science, Michael Ruse, in a review in *Trends in Ecology and Evolution*, praised unreservedly the computerised phrase-building exercise, and went on to refer to the even 'more wonderful things' of the tree-graphics figures.[91]

What are we to make of this extraordinary state of affairs, with a respected and influential author, eulogised on the dust cover of his latest book as 'one of the most brilliant of the rising generation of biologists', putting forward in all seriousness, badly flawed arguments in support of his views? I have been deeply intrigued by this strange happening, and after much thought have come to the conclusion that the answer probably lies in a point made by Francis Bacon some 400 years ago, to the effect that once a proposition has been established in the understanding, thereafter everything new is made to support it; either the new is not observed, or it is rejected on one pretext or another, rather than admit exceptions to the established proposition. This seems to be what has happened to Dawkins and his reviewers; they have become so deeply immured in the doctrines of evolutionary theory that they have become psychologically incapable of noticing anything that threatens to subvert these doctrines.

Apart from these misconceptions a pivotal feature of Dawkins' whole case is the assumption that any complex structure, which could not possibly have evolved in a single giant step, could quite easily evolve in a long series of finely graded cumulative steps, provided only that each step is sufficiently small and brings some slight advantage over the preceding step. He concludes his book with the dogmatic assertion: 'No matter how improbable it is that an X could have arisen from a Y in a single step, it is always possible to conceive of a series of infinitesimally graded intermediates between them . . . and provided we postulate a sufficiently large series of finely graded intermediates we shall be able to derive anything from anything else without invoking astronomical improbabilities'. This pronouncement may sound reasonable at first sight, but a little thought shows it to be quite untrue. As noted in the previous chapter, the eye-focusing mechanism is one example of something that could not have evolved in a series of non-sequential discrete steps interspersed with many more useless or harmful steps.

Consider the eye a little more fully. It is not an autonomous self-sufficient unit, although evolutionists tend to treat it as such. It is totally useless without the brain, of which it is really an extension. The first stage in the brain is the optic chiasma, which collates the millions of fibres in the optic nerves into two groups carrying signals from the left and right visual half-fields of both eyes, and passing them on, via the left and right lateral geniculate bodies, to the primary visual cortex and thence to secondary, tertiary, quaternary, and limbic areas of the brain. Despite Dawkins' optimistic words, it is surely quite evident that this ingenious little cross-over unit, together with the associated complex brain circuitry involving *billions* of co-operating nerve cells, could never have evolved in a long series of discrete steps. Nor does it seem even remotely likely that it might have started existence in an incipient form adapted to some other purpose, an 'explanation' often advanced by evolutionists.

I find this example quite conclusive, but those who don't, may find an analogy more forceful. Consider a manufactured article, say

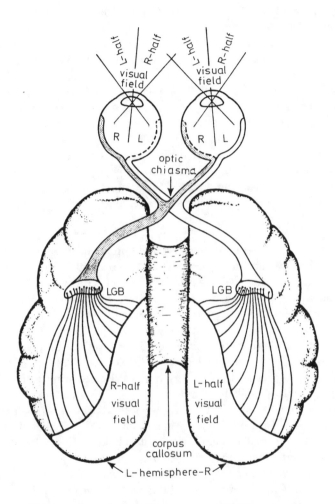

Figure 3 Diagram, reproduced from *The Human Mystery* by John Eccles, of visual pathways showing the left-half and right-half visual fields with the retinal images and the partial crossing in the optic chiasma so that the right-half of the visual field of each eye goes to left visual cortex, after relay in the lateral geniculate body (*LGB*), and correspondingly for left visual field to right visual cortex.

for instance a bicycle. Provided you are not too critical, it is easy to imagine the front wheel of an ancestral pennyfarthing machine getting gradually smaller, and the rear wheel larger, with the eventual result that you end up with both wheels the same size, and, hopefully, a suitably modified frame. But then a snag arises. In order to avoid the need for absurdly fast pedalling, you have to add a step-up gearing system, comprising a pair of chain wheels and a matching chain, arranged so that the rear wheel rotates faster than the pedal shaft. The point is, it is *quite impossible to do this in a long series of tiny intermediate steps*. Isolated bits of chain or sprocket would be worse than useless, and you *must* introduce a pair of sprockets of identical tooth pitch and suitable ratio, plus a matching chain of correct length, and a pedal shaft with bearing and pedals, all at the same time.

If this analogy sounds too contrived, as Dawkins has assured me it does[92], then consider a simpler case, the humble bicycle pump. The pump *must* be introduced or evolved by creating all the essential functional elements – the barrel, the piston with its handle, the flexible connector to attach to the tyre valve – at the same time. They could not be added piecemeal, independently of each other; each part would be quite useless without the others. In fact I cannot think of *any* object where this principle would not apply, unless possibly it be something very simple like a one-piece wooden clothes-peg. Nor, for that matter, can I think of any biological mechanism where the same principle is unlikely to apply.

When I first raised this difficulty with Dr Dawkins, he dismissed it as a special case not having general validity, but I should have thought the general principle was quite obvious. It can be stated very simply: *functionally interacting elements of a biological mechanism must come into existence simultaneously, or concurrently, if it is to function properly, and it is therefore highly unlikely that they can evolve in a long series of discrete non-sequential intermediate steps*. This principle cannot be negated by arguing that the mechanism might have originated in a simpler form adapted to a different purpose, and only later developed into its final form, since in most cases the principle must apply at *some* stage of reaching the final form, and in any case the original function would itself probably involve the same principle.

To sum up, it seems entirely reasonable to conclude that the type of non-sequential cumulative selection demonstrated by Dawkins in the computerised phrase-building exercise, is highly unlikely to occur in biological evolution. He *might* respond by saying 'All right, so I made a mistake in overlooking the absence of sequence control, but that does not invalidate my essential point, which is simply that *cumulative* selection eliminates the problem of the astronomical improbabilities of single-step spontaneous selection. What is wrong with the idea of *sequential* cumulative selection?' The answer to this is, it doesn't really help. In what way can the time factor affect the probabilities? Does it make any difference whether the process is done quickly or slowly? Dawkins' doodling exercise illustrates this clearly; he could easily duplicate any of his 'biomorphs' by simply repeating the sequence of 'gene' changes, irrespective of the period of time allowed. It would not make the slightest difference to the result if he introduced the changes once every millisecond or once every month. The sequence is the deciding factor, and the time taken is irrelevant. And conversely, if in the phrase-building exercise the characters had to appear in strict sequence from first to last, the odds against would remain at the Dawkins single-shot figure of 27^{28} to 1, regardless of the time taken.

Conceivably circumstances might *sometimes* arise in which a slow gradual accumulation of changes involves less improbability than a sudden occurrence of the same changes, or in which strict sequentiality is not essential; but if so, I think they would have been very few and far between. In the great majority of cases in the world of biology, it seems to me that strict sequentiality would have been an essential factor, and the time factor would have been virtually irrelevant to the probabilities involved. As I remarked above, what Dawkins has *really* demonstrated, and demonstrated quite brilliantly, is the power of willed direction to control the outcome of mutational changes. Although quite unintended, this is highly significant and valuable, as we shall find later in this book.

41

CHAPTER IV

SOME PRACTICAL PROBLEMS

Problems animate and inanimate. Order, pattern, beauty. Colour.
Personal incredulity. Preconceptions. The blind eye.

Many books are available dealing with the practical difficulties of
evolutionary theory, and there is no shortage of things which it
cannot explain. Here I will mention only a few of the less publicised
instances.

Consider the order lepidoptera, or butterflies and moths, thought
to have evolved from a primitive wingless ancestor some 350 million
years ago.[40] As we all know, the butterfly starts life as a tiny hard-
shelled egg within which an embryo grows and eats its way out to
become a voracious caterpillar which proceeds to gorge itself on our
vegetation. When fully grown, the caterpillar sheds its skin for the
last time, and changes into a pupa or chrysalis containing an
amorphous mass of tissues which somehow rebuilds itself –
metamorphoses – into a totally different structure having a totally
different lifestyle. The contrast between caterpillar and butterfly
could not be more unpredictable and fantastic. Are we really
expected to believe that this mysterious metamorphosis could have
been the outcome of fortuitous genetic mutations, mere accidental
mishaps, in the genes of the ancestral wingless form? Genetic
mutations could conceivably have resulted in the evolution of a sort
of supercaterpillar, but it is an insult to our intelligence to insist that

they resulted in a butterfly. And apart from the enormous improbability of such an occurrence, where is the survival advantage in this drastic change of form? Caterpillars have developed very effective and ingenious methods of coping with predators, so why throw all this away and adopt a dramatic form of self-advertisement at great cost?

Darwin freely admitted that if any complex structure existed which could not have been formed by numerous successive slight modifications, his theory would have been invalidated. It would be hard to find a more clear-cut example than the butterfly, with its numerous problems of structural rebuilding during metamorphosis, involving thousands of co-ordinated changes which could not possibly evolve non-sequentially. And Dawkins himself has emphasised the impossibly vast odds against spontaneous evolution in one giant step.

Ironically, Dawkins also objects strongly to those who are unable to accept freely all the improbabilities involved in Darwinian evolution. In his book he lambasts the Bishop of Birmingham for expressing doubts about the effectiveness of natural selection.[19/38] He accuses the Bishop of making 'heavy use of The Argument from Personal Incredulity', asserting that this is 'an extremely weak argument'. He seems to have turned a blind eye to the plain fact that Darwinian evolutionary theory is in essence a speculative, conjectural, theory, unproved and unprovable. As such, it *is* entirely a matter of credibility, of credulity or incredulity by the individual. It seems to me that credulous acceptance of Dawkins' assertion that anything can evolve from anything else, provided a sufficient number of finely graded intermediate steps be allowed, is more irrational than the hard-headed, incredulous rejection of the assertion.

Consider now the honey-bee, a recently-evolved insect dating back only some twenty-five million years.[42] Does it make sense to think that its ability to secrete a special wax, and build it into a beautifully engineered comb to house and feed its young, was the outcome of a long series of fortuitous genetic mishaps? Was it just by good luck that the wax was of exactly the right consistency, neither too brittle nor too soft, the first time it was accidentally produced?

Or if the right qualities had to evolve, how did they do so? More accidents? And does it begin to make sense to say that the famous 'waggle dance', used to inform fellow workers in the hive of the direction, distance, and magnitude of a newly discovered food supply, resulted from an accumulation of genetic mishaps? These are not rhetorical questions, they are serious questions meriting careful thought by everyone interested in the momentous implications of Darwinism, which ought to mean every thinking person who has been taught to believe in the theory of evolution.

I turn now to the extraordinary story of 'Sirex and Ibalia.'[20] The wood wasp *sirex* bores a hole in the trunk of a conifer for its eggs. The emergent grubs feed on the wood, boring a tunnel in which they live for some years before turning into a wasp with powerful jaws which are used to bite its way out of the tree. Now comes the villain of the piece, the *ibalia*, a parasitic hymenopter which, using the holes provided by the wasp, lays its eggs inside the wasp grubs. When they hatch, these larvae feed on the wasp grubs, taking care not to devour the vital organs until the other parts have been eaten! When the wasp grub has the parasitic larva inside itself, it changes its habit of deep boring, and starts to burrow towards the surface, thus helping the parasitic larva to escape from the tree. Sheer drama!

It is surely quite inconceivable that the slow accumulation of advantageous random mutations should result in a) *ibalia*'s habit of depositing its eggs in the wasp grubs; b) the parasitic larva's habit of keeping its host alive as long as possible by eating the non-vital parts first; c) the impregnated grub's habit of changing its tunneling direction so as to aid the parasite which devours it. Each of these inter-dependent items of strange behaviour seems inexplicable in terms of fortuitous variations, let alone all three together. Clearly the Dawkins brand of cumulative selection cannot apply to this sort of co-operative sequential modification.

Another case of synergetic mutual aid behaviour is that of the parasitic trematode which infects an ant but has to pass to a sheep's liver in order to reproduce.[72] The chance of an infected ant being eaten by a sheep is obviously very small, so the ant obligingly crawls to the tip of a blade of grass to await a grazing sheep. It would be interesting to hear a Darwinian explanation of how it was that the trematode managed to survive until it accidentally found a way of persuading ants to commit suicide!

It is ironic that the prevalence of unattractive parasitic behaviour in the world of nature (of which innumerable further examples could easily be quoted) can also be seen as an argument in support of evolution, inasmuch as it seems incompatible with the alternative of deliberate creation by a benign agency. It seems to have been this argument that persuaded Darwin to formulate his theory of evolution in the first place, as we shall find in a later chapter. But although many people find the argument persuasive, further thought brings to mind equally persuasive counter-arguments which I will discuss later.

A fascinating example of synergetic behaviour is provided by the beetle *oncideres*, the female of which seeks out a mimosa tree, ignoring all other trees.[90] She climbs the tree, crawls along a limb, and cuts a longitudinal slit with her mandible, then deposits her eggs in the slit. She then backs up a foot or so and proceeds to girdle the limb by cutting down to the cambrium, a job which takes her several hours. She then departs. The girdled limb eventually falls to the ground and rots. The beetle larvae feed happily on the rotting wood (they are unable to survive on live wood). Apart from providing food for larvae, the tree itself benefits from the beetle's activities. Mimosa trees normally live for some twenty-five to thirty years, but when pruned annually they can survive for up to a century.

Lyall Watson mentions, in one of his interesting books, the amazing disguise system of the Amazon plant-hopper insect.[94] It is some three to four inches in length, and is related to the aphids and cicadas. It feeds on the sap of rivers-edge plants. It has white 'false-teeth' in accurate bas-relief, and looks so much like a baby alligator as to fool even a naturalist.

Another astonishing performance is provided by the flattid bug insect, a colony of which disguises itself as a life-like imitation of a coral-coloured flower something like a hyacinth, with a green tip, then a row of partially-mature flowers, and the remainder as mature red flowers.[1] When disturbed this 'flower' dissolves into a cloud of large moth-like insects. They then regroup on a dead twig, and crawl over each other to re-form a perfect imitation flower, with green tip, half green and pale coral next, and finally dark coral and red outermost. It would be very interesting to learn how this might have come about as an outcome of naturally selected random mutations.

I cannot close this brief review of some of the practical difficulties of biological evolution without discussing what is, I think, the biggest problem of them all, although strangely enough it never seems to get mentioned in most books in this field. It is unique, and crucially important, in that it is common to *all* life, and moreover is known to everybody from a combination of explicit television documentaries and intimate personal experience. I refer to the reproductive system, which is an intrinsic pivotal feature of *all* life, whether human, animal or vegetable. Perhaps we have a classic case of 'familiarity breeds contempt'.

It is a basic axiom of orthodox evolutionary theory that all biological structures have evolved from more primitive beginnings, by the long-continued natural selection of any advantageous variations that happened to become available. Richard Dawkins, for instance, rightly stresses the point that even a crude primordial eye would have been better than no eye at all, and could (or so he claims) quite easily evolve into a more efficient modern eye by natural processes. And the same thing could be said of other organs and structures, whether eye or ear, nose or lung, arm or wing, scale or feather, etc. A fair case of half a loaf being better than no bread! This *seems* a reasonable argument which can be seen as the ground or foundation of evolution, until it is realised that there is at least one glaring exception to it, namely the reproductive system. It would be absurd, to say the least, to claim that an incipient half-baked reproductive system would be better than no system at all. Emphatically *not* a case of half an embryo being better than none! The system *must* work the first time and every time, otherwise life would have been impossible.

A few of the features which *must all be present* if the mammalian reproductive system is to function properly are as follows:

a) A gametogenital system (gonads), of ovary and testes, to manufacture the female ova and male spermatozoa having only half the normal number of chromosomes.

b) Sperm cells to be motile, with the ability and instinct to seek out the waiting ovum.

c) The male body to have a biological mechanism for implanting the sperm in the body of the female.

d) The ovum accepts a single sperm, and immediately blocks the entry of any further sperm.

e) The sperm cell unites with the ovum in such manner as will ensure ordered blending of the nuclear chromosomes and genes.

f) The zygote or fertilised ovum initiates a process of cell division and proliferation. This is something it has never done before and therefore cannot learn by experience.

g) The growing embryo acquires a placenta and umbilicus to serve as a channel to conduct blood and waste products between mother and embryo.

h) The foetus is expelled from the uterus or womb at full term, and continues to grow in the external world until growth stops at maturity, with cell-proliferating activity greatly reduced to only the level required to replace moribund or injured cells.

i) Mammary glands manufacture, and supply to the new-born babe, liquid nourishment in the form of mother's milk.

The above is far from being a comprehensive list of all the inter-related factors involved, but I think it serves to indicate something of the magnitude of the problem. Those interested in studying the whole thing more fully would find Smith and William's book useful.[86]

Doubtless some of these features, particularly those involving the male animal, first evolved prior to the emergence of the mammals, but this is beside the point, it merely pushes the problem further back in time. I referred to the placental mammalian system because of our familiarity with it, and strictly speaking I should have referred to the *first* animal, whether classified as reptile or vertebrate or whatever, to use the same sort of system as that used by Homo sapiens. The real question is, how did the *first not-previously-existent* reproductive system evolve? Obviously it had to work the first time it was used, otherwise the user could have left no descendents. Yet it would have shown no advantage to prior life forms and could not have been selected for survival advantage. Are we to assume that it must have evolved during the breeding life-time of the original user? A pretty problem for the evolutionists.

A further point is whether in actual fact the improbability of single-step evolution of a system of inter-dependent parts and units, is reduced if, instead of taking place suddenly or spontaneously, it is allowed to take place over a long period of time. At first sight this assumption sounds reasonable, but is it really valid? If evolution of the mammalian reproductive system required say 1000 steps (probably a gross under-estimate), each of which had to take place in a specific sequence, would it make any difference if the whole process was completed in a millisecond or a millennium? I think not. The deciding factor is the sequentiality, not the time taken. (Refer again to page 41 above.) Admittedly it seems sensible to think that gradual cumulative selection over a long period of time is less improbable than spontaneous 'single step' selection, but is it really true? I throw the question open to discussion by those interested.

It would be easy to give further instances of strange behaviour and ingenious structure in the animal world, and indeed many have been quoted by other writers. See for instance references 89 and 105. Evolutionists seem to have evolved a strange ability to disregard them. Perhaps a change to the plant world will awaken interest. Consider the dodder plant, a leafless parasitic plant of the genus *Cuscuta*, having fang-like mid-stem roots which it sinks into the victim's flesh to suck their life blood or sap.[62] The dodder emerges from the soil as a tendril-like stem which grows rapidly and appears to look around in search of prey, probably using shade-seeking cells on the growing tip. In a few hours it turns towards a suitable sapling or thick-stemmed plant, and in a few days coils round it much like a snake, and proceeds to sink its fangs into the sap channels. Once having 'tasted blood', it withdraws completely from the soil, and continues to live on the unfortunate host, perfectly able to withdraw and advance to an adjoining host with a stronger appeal. None of the dodder's special features, its shade-seeking guide cells, its lack of leaves, its centrally sited fang-roots, would have been useful on their own, yet the chance of them evolving simultaneously must surely have been vanishingly small.

Consider too the carnivorous plants, such as the pitcher plants, which drown their victims in water treated with wetting agent.[25] The internal surfaces of the pitcher above the water level are very slippery, and coated with appetising nectar which tempts the unwary prey to graze, during which activity he slips lower and lower and eventually falls and drowns, followed in due course by digestion and absorption into the plant tissues. But this is not the end of a strange story. There is a variety of mosquito which drops its eggs into the decaying debris at the bottom of the pitcher, the larva being equipped with special feet able to grip the slippery slopes and crawl out. One wonders how many unfortunate larvae drowned before chance took a hand and provided them with the non-slip feet! And did chance also provide the pitcher plant with its gift of a special wetting agent?

Another major problem for evolutionary theory is to account for the unnecessarily high degree of order and pattern in nature, for the sheer beauty of form and colouration going well beyond any conceivable survival value. Consider one of the more obvious examples, the peacock's tail. Is it remotely credible that fortuitous genetic mutations could have resulted in the spectacular display of iridescent colour? If we saw random splashes of colour on canvas, we could legitimately assume that they got there by accident, but if we saw a pattern or design we would *know* with certainty that it was the result of deliberate effort. Why then should we give credence to the extraordinary view that the design of a peacock's tail was the outcome of accident? Darwin was conscious of this problem; he once wrote to Asa Gray '. . . small trifling particulars of structure often make me very uncomfortable. The sight of a feather in a peacock's tail, whenever I gaze at it, makes me sick'.[35]

And how about the peahen? Are we to believe that she can experience colour sensation, and accidentally acquired an aesthetic sense sufficiently developed to appreciate the spectacular tail display? Does it not seem probable that she would have responded to random splashes of colour just as well? And in any case, is there any reason to assume that the most decorative peacocks would foster the fittest or most plentiful chicks?

The peacock's tail is only one example of innumerable instances of 'beauty beyond the call of duty' throughout the world of nature. Think of the butterfly wing, the brilliant tropical fish, the sea-shell, the wild flower, etc. Those who would dispute the validity of the argument on the grounds that beauty is in the eye of the beholder rather than being an independent reality, are merely re-phrasing it; they are saying that chance can account for the ability of the beholder to see beauty in the beholden, instead of accounting for the beauty itself.

Talking of beauty and colour, let us now discuss colour more fully. Scientists from Newton onwards have maintained that colour is purely a mental sensation devoid of objective physical existence. As Newton put it, 'the rays are not coloured'. How then did colour originate? Could it have *evolved* in any way? How can something not having physical reality evolve? We know very little about the nature of colour, apart from the fact that it is somehow related to the wavelength or frequency of light. We do not have the remotest idea what the relationship is, and cannot even imagine what it might be. The two things, colour and wavelength, seem totally disparate; in different categories of existence. There is nothing in the operations of physics and chemistry to suggest a relationship between these two different things. The only way we can define colour is by saying that it is the name given to the mental sensation which arises when the eye is stimulated by a partial spectrum of light wavelengths.

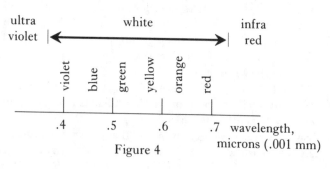

Figure 4

We know that the colour sensation resulting from a given stimulus is always the same, and we have every reason to think it is the same for everybody with normal colour vision, because we all seem to agree on colour clashes and harmonies, and in any case it would be absurd to think that either evolution or creation might have provided every individual with a different range of colours. This fixed unvarying relationship between colour and wavelength or frequency, seems to imply the existence of a universal *principle* of colour. It is hard to see what it could be, and it seems to me that if it is physical, it can only be explained as a property or characteristic of light photons (elementary units or quanta of light), which causes or enables them to evoke the mental sensation of colour. After all, colour must have existed in *some* form prior to the evolution of colour vision, since it can hardly be said that evolution evolved means to perceive something which did not exist. Or did colour appear as if by magic, *ex nihilo*, after colour vision evolved? I doubt if even a convinced evolutionist would claim this!

Whichever way we look at it, we seem to be faced with a major problem. On the one hand, if we regard the objective physical world as the only reality, there is the problem of how the photons of light came to have their colour-evoking property (or if you prefer the expression, how colour came to be a component of colourless white light). Alternatively, if the postulate of a non-physical realm be accepted, and the aforesaid universal principle of colour be regarded as non-physical, then there is the problem of what the principle *is*, and how it originated. In the former case, it seems impossible to conceive of the colour-evoking property originating in random variations in any sort of physical structure, and we are forced to the conclusion that it must have been introduced when the universe itself originated, long before the means of colour perception evolved. Either it got there accidentally, or else it was deliberately put there. I do not think the most rabid evolutionist would claim the former, so we are left with the latter – deliberate introduction or imbuing. Obviously we cannot say what sort of agency could have achieved such a feat, and can say only that it must have completely transcended any conceivable human potentiality. In the second case

51

– that of non-physical effects – we can say nothing except to appeal to a transcendental agency again. Thus it seems that either way we come to the same conclusion, which is that evolutionary theory cannot account for the existence of colour sensation.

Consider next the evolution of *colour vision*. The primordial visual organ was simply a light-sensitive spot on the epidermis, providing rudimentary sensing of lightness and darkness. Then came an optical eye, having either a pinhole or a lens focused on a photo-receptor screen or retina responsive to the visible octave of radiant energy, to provide monochromatic image-forming vision. Later, some of the photo-receptor cells in the retina were segregated into three separate groups differentially reponsive to selected wavebands in the visible spectrum, accompanied by corresponding changes in the complex neural circuitry of the brain. In this way our three-colour principle of colour vision arose. It is self-evidently impossible that this highly coordinated segregation exercise could have been the outcome of non-sequential discrete mutations of the type postulated by Dawkins. He instances the way in which colour on a television screen can be gradually improved by slowly turning the control knob, as indicating that colour vision might have evolved gradually, but I find the analogy irrelevant.[19/84] As I see it, colour vision could only have evolved in the 'all-or-nothing' fashion which as Dawkins himself explains, involves impossibly vast odds against success. Even if it be postulated that colour sensation was first confined to a single colour, which sounds pretty unlikely, this would still have involved concurrent segregation of retinal cells and brain cells, which could not be done in non-sequential steps. In fact three such major stages, one each for the three primary colours, would surely magnify the difficulties and improbabilities instead of reducing them.

There is one more aspect of colour which merits examination, that of how the partial spectra of light waves which stimulate the sensation of colour, originated. Daylight contains all the visible wavelengths of light, and when some of these wavelengths are filtered out, colours are evoked, as we saw above. This filtering is caused by energy interactions between the incident photons of light and the electrons in the outer electron clouds of the surface being viewed. The only difference between one photon and another is their energy level. Pigments are substances whose outer electrons interact energetically with photons and selectively absorb those in certain wavebands. For instance, a red pigment is one which absorbs high-energy short-wave photons in the blue end of the spectrum, and reflects mainly those in the low-energy long-wave red end. The question is, how did it come about that the relative energy levels of electrons and light photons are such as to bring about this selective absorption and reflection activity, resulting in the partial spectra needed to evoke the sensation of colour? It would be stretching coincidence to incredible lengths to assume that when electrons and light photons came into existence at the beginning of the universe, aeons before visual organs existed, their energy just happened by chance to be what was later needed to cause the partial spectra necessary for colour production. It has been argued that there is nothing remarkable about the colour-producing properties of pigments; they are simply a part of the infinite variety of natural phenomena which organisms turn to their advantage. No mystery, just one more example of the natural tendency of life to make use of whatever there is in nature that can provide advantage. I don't dispute it. All I am saying is that this particular phenomenon, of colour-producing properties of pigments, cannot have arisen by Darwinian processes of the selection of random variations.

It has also been argued that colour is simply the organism's way of interpreting light frequency (the reciprocal of wavelength), just as music is its way of interpreting sound frequency. That is one way of putting it, certainly, but it tells us nothing about the nature and origin of colour, and is irrevelant to my point that colour could not have evolved by Darwinian processes. The same could be said of another argument, advanced by no less authoritative a source than the scientific journal *Nature*, saying that 'colour is an interpretation of surface reflectance', and before the advent of organisms able to perceive colour, 'there was *no* colour'.[92] So evolution achieved the impossible feat of evolving means of perceiving something which did not exist! How blind can science get?

Another argument I have heard, is that colour could have been useful in the very early stages of vision using only a light-sensitive spot, but it is hard to see how this could have worked. Colour is displayed by individual objects within the whole visual field of view, and its perception requires an optical system providing a defined *image* which distinguishes individual objects. Colour vision might have been achieved with a pin-hole eye, but not with a single light-sensitive spot devoid of image-forming properties.

It seems to me abundantly clear that any one of the foregoing examples – butterfly, bee, wood wasp, trematode, *oncideres*, plant-hopper, flattid bug, reproductive system, dodder, pitcher plant, and colour – suffices to throw very grave doubt on the claimed universal efficacy of Neo-Darwinian evolutionary theory, despite the forth-right dismissal of personal incredulity by Dawkins. Those who agree with his dismissal should remind themselves that if personal incredulity of evolution can be dismissed so freely, then by the same token, so can personal incredulity of the alternative of Creation. Sauce for the goose . . .! As I said before, evolution is a speculative theory not capable of being proven or disproven, and can be validated only by its credibility. Personal credulity or incredulity is the only way it *can* be judged.

There may be those who, whilst avoiding the Dawkinsian traps, will nevertheless manage to fudge the issue by dint of evasive semantics and sophistry, but I doubt their ability to refute, in plain direct words, the practical points I have made above. I speak from personal experience of the near-insuperable difficulty of persuading members of the Establishments to give open-minded consideration to heterodox views of long-standing professional doctrines and dogmas. As John Evans commented in a recent book 'Unfortunately, once the conscious mind has been caught up in some orthodox consensus of thought, it becomes extremely resistant to change. All strong dogmatic belief, particularly if inculcated early in life, is to some extent self-fulfilling; and at a certain mental level, it would seem that truth and belief are largely synonymous'.[26] And it is not only the conscious mind that can mislead or blind us to truth; as Willis Harman has pointed out in a deeply thoughtful book, we are all liable to be misled or biased by our *un*conscious beliefs and preconceptions.[32] This must apply to me as much as everybody else, of course, but forewarned is forearmed, and at least I *try* to be open-minded.

As I mentioned earlier, evolutionists seem to have evolved a special sort of eye, a blind eye, which they press into use when confronted with things their theory finds unaccountable. They prefer to support their case with examples such as moths which adapt their colouration to the prevailing colour of tree trunks, or insects which develop resistance to insecticides, and so on – examples which although valid as far as they go, avoid explaining the problem of structures having functionally inter-related parts that have come into existence concurrently or sequentially.

CHAPTER V

SPECIATION AND EXTINCTION

Punctuated prodigiousity. 4,950 million failed species. Extinction the norm, speciation the puzzle. Vigour and vitality factor.

The whole evolution controversy was sparked off by the publication in 1859 of Charles Darwin's *The Origin of Species*. Actually, the book dealt mainly with evolution of improved features in organisms by the natural selection of advantageous variations, and said very little about its title matter, the origin of species. It *implied* that the long-continued gradual accumulation of small changes would eventually, given enough time, result in large differences amounting to a new species unable to interbreed with the original form. Darwin had been persuaded by Lyell's *Principles of Geology* that sufficient time had in fact been available. He realised that evidence for his theory would have to come from the fossil record, and was worried by the almost complete absence of fossils of the innumerable transitional forms implied by his theory. However, he assumed that time would bring these missing links to light in due course, and it was this hope that sustained his belief in the theory.

This hope was not to be fulfilled, either in his lifetime or afterwards. Many biologists have been forced to admit this. For instance G. G. Simpson has said 'The absence of transitional forms is an almost universal phenomenon'.[87Q] More recently, Prof. R. J. Berry has said 'Notwithstanding the well-documented occurrence of many transitional forms, there is no denying the fact that they are rare'.[5] And Mark Ridley 'The most striking thing about [fossils showing evolutionary change] is their rarity . . . . It has been known for over a century that fossil lineages generally appear suddenly in the fossil record, persist for a few million years, and then disappear abruptly without merging into later lineages'.[74]

It seems to be generally accepted that the number of species extant at any one time is in the region of a few million, and it has been said that this figure is a good deal less than one per cent of the total number of species ever produced,[55] which suggests that the grand total must run into billions. G. R. Taylor gives a range of estimates varying from one and a half to sixteen billion,[89] and Murchie suggests a figure of five billion.[62] Taylor also suggests a rough overall average figure of one million years for the life of a species, and a like figure has been advanced by other writers. If we accept Murchie's figure of five billion total species, and assume that most of them were produced during the last 600 million years since the beginning of the Cambrian age, this gives an overall rate of speciation of about 1000 new species per century. But species do not arise at a steady rate, they tend to come in great outbursts, and the actual rate of speciation must considerably exceed the overall average, probably running into tens of thousands per century.

An attempt to resolve the puzzle presented by the abrupt appearance and disappearance of species has been made by the Americans, Niles Eldridge and Stephen Gould, who postulate a modification of Darwinism in which short periods of speciation and extinction are interpersed between longer periods of stasis. They named this scheme Punctuated Equilibria, and Figure 5A shows in stylised form a typical cycle. In a total of 600 million years, some fifty such cycles could occur, meeting the estimate of a grand total of five billion new species produced. One difficulty with this scheme is that it implies a far greater number of extant species than the generally agreed figure of a few million. Another difficulty is that it conflicts with the suppositional average species-life in the region of a million years. These difficulties could be removed by a modified version of the scheme, as indicated by Figure 5B, in which

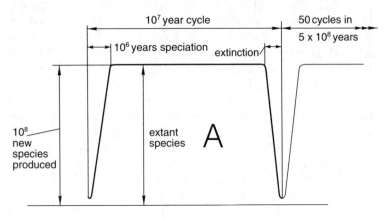

Figure 5A   Typical Punctuated Equilibria Cycle

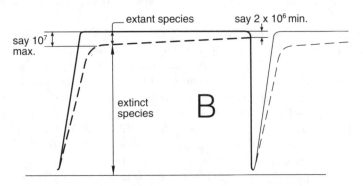

Figure 5B   Proposed Speciation/Extinction Cycle

NB. These diagrams are stylised representations of general trends only, without pretence to quantitative accuracy.

extinction more or less keeps pace with speciation instead of being confined to the end of the cycle. However, this does not remove *all* problems, to put it mildly.

According to Ernst Mayr, one of the founders of Neo-Darwinism, speciation usually involves geographical isolation, and the time required for a new species to evolve can be anything from a few hundred to few million years.[55] Assuming a conservative mean of, say, 10,000 years, then if species evolved one-at-a-time, this would give only 100 new species in the million-year active speciation period of Figure 5A. To provide the 100 million new species in each cycle, and the grand total of five billion in the 600 million year span, requires that a *million* species evolve *together*, or simultaneously, in a million isolated ecological niches. Quite a vista! It is not suggested that this figure be taken literally, since we do not know the basic factors with any accuracy, but I think it represents a fair picture of the sort of problem involved in the origin of species – problems not envisaged by, or knowable to, Charles Darwin.

Not all biologists are sold on the Punctuated Equilibria theory, although all seem to agree that speciation is not a steady continuous process, but occurs in sudden explosive bursts in all, or most, of the major geographical epochs, the Cambrian, Devonian, Permian, Triassic, Createcous, etc. Strictly speaking, these major outbursts ought to be superimposed on the relatively minor cycles of the Punctuationist scheme, and each phyla, or at least each major group – such as plants, trees, insects, small animals, large animals – ought to have its own cycles, but this is hardly practicable, and in any case will not affect the overall result. The basic factors involved in determining the number of simultaneous speciations are three: 1) the grand total of all species produced, 2) the *average* time required to produce a species, and 3) the *total active* speciation time available. Then to find the number of species that have to evolve simultaneously, simply multiply items 1 and 2 together, divide by item 3, and you have the answer. Thus for the case given, multiply the grand total of *five billion* species by the *average* speciation time of *10,000* years, divide by the *total active* speciation time of *fifty million* years, and you get the figure of one million simultaneous speciations, as before. As will be seen from this, the number, length, and magnitude of the individual cycles is irrelevant, what matters are the totals.

Obviously we cannot know the *average* time required for a species to evolve with any certainty; and the total active speciation time is also something of a guess. If for instance, the supposed average time for a species to evolve is reduced from 10,000 years to say 3,000 years, and the total active time is increased from 50 million years to say 150 million, this reduces the number of simultaneous speciations from one million to 100,000. There is also the point that speciation may not start and stop with absolute abruptness, and there could well be a more or less continuous small flow of speciation underlying the peak active periods. One way and another, its seems reasonable to think that the graph of the number of species evolving simultaneously will be a continuous curve falling to near, but not quite, zero between the active outburst periods, and peaking at a figure of perhaps a few 100,000 in the middle of each outburst. Even so, although less spectacular than the original estimate of 1,000,000, it is still an extraordinary figure.

Another point, easily overlooked, is that a biological organism is a highly complex combination of many cooperating parts and units, of bone, muscle, cartilage, glands, tissues, skin and blood; and of many sub-systems, such as the circulatory, respiratory, alimentary, endocrine, reproductive and auto-immune, plus sensory organs. It seems reasonable to think that of all the genetic mutations occurring in an organism, no more than one in several hundreds will relate to a particular feature of that organism. And as we have already noted, it seems probable that only one in many thousands of *these* will be advantageous. All of which means that *less than one in a million* of all the mutations occurring in an organism is likely to be usable for a particular item of evolution. And don't forget that mutations of any sort are extremely rare, mere copying mishaps in a mechanism noted for its extremely high degree of replicative accuracy, far exceeding anything achieved in man's mass-production manufacture. It begins to look as though Darwinian evolutionary theory is not a very credible explanation of the billions of species that have appeared on earth.

As we have already noted, it is necessary for mutations to occur in a specific functional *sequence* if they are to result in the evolution of a structure having a number of inter-connected components. Even so simple a thing as an eyelid comes into this category. So what are the prospects of a complete physiological or neurological structure evolving in a long series of unrelated steps *each* separated from the preceding step by many thousands or millions of harmful or irrelevant mutations? Absolutely nil, I suggest.

Consider just one simple example, the flatfish. It is thought that once the fish acquired the habit of sleeping on its side on the sea-bed, the downwards-facing eye gradually migrated round the head to the other, upwards-facing, side, with obvious advantage to the fish. But what possible advantage could have accrued from the early stages of the eye-migration, when it had perhaps moved only a very small distance? There are countless examples of this sort of practical problem, quite apart from the numerical problems we have seen above. For instance, what advantage would accrue to a reptile half-way transformed into a bird? Or to a bird having wings and feathers but lacking the stronger heart and more active metabolism needed to supply the energy for flight, or lacking even the flight-muscle structure, plus the lightened skeleton and lowered centre of gravity, etc.? What would be the advantage of a forelimb half transformed into a wing? It is hard to think of a case of advantageous adaptation free from this sort of difficulty, which can be stated broadly as 'How can natural selection possibly act upon the useless early stages of a new or improved feature?' Plenty more examples can be found by those who would seek them and a book I can recommend for this purpose is G. R. Taylor's *The Great Evolution Mystery*.[89] For myself, I find the numerical facts of the case suffice to throw grave doubts on the validity of Darwin's belief in the power of natural selection of random variations. In fact I would go further, and say anybody who can ponder the foregoing facts without becoming incredulous of Darwinism as an explanation of the coming into existence of billions of separate species, has been thoroughly brain-washed. As Mark Ridley observed with understatement, 'Speciation is rich in problems but poor in solutions'.[74]

This, however, is only half of the overall problem. We have to account not only for the great outbursts of speciation, but also for the extraordinary rate of extinction. Extant species were disappearing almost as rapidly as new species were arriving. If the basis of evolution is gradual adaptation to a changing environment as Darwin claimed, then it is reasonable to expect established species to be very well adapted to their current environment, and indeed, many biologists have remarked on the stability of species, sometimes running into hundreds of millions of years. Thus one would expect an established species not to die out until some major environmental upset occurred. Ernst Mayr states firmly that the primary determinant in the rise and fall of species is the interaction between organism and environment, and that the frequency of extinction is a great puzzle.[55]

But there is another way of looking at the problem. We have seen that the vast majority of mutations are harmful rather than beneficial, perhaps in the ratio of thousands or tens of thousands to one (see page 29), and seen in that light it is reasonable to think that the overall effect of mutational change will be towards a *decrease* rather than an increase, in the number, variety, and complexity of species. If it is the fittest that survive best, we should surely expect to finish up with a relatively small number of robust, simple, versatile species, rather than a very large number of ever more specialised complex species. Seen from this viewpoint, the real puzzle is the *proliferation* of species, rather than their extinction.

The broad picture seen by Darwinians is of a very large number of species of every imaginable variety, constantly diversified and expanded by the natural selection of random genetic mutations, with the total number kept within the limits that the biosphere can handle, by a mysterious process of regular extinction.

The contrary picture I see, is one of *too many* species, precariously balanced between survival and extinction, fighting hard for food and shelter and avoidance of predators, while at the same time subject to continual mutational changes which almost invariably hinder them in the struggle to survive, until finally they succumb. Opposing this implacable drift towards extinction is a mysterious positive force which acts periodically to replenish the depleted stock of extant species. John Davidson has made the same point, saying that it seems as if some unknown 'vitality and vigour' factor comes into play periodically, to replenish the depleted stock of species.[80] And G. R. Taylor was led to conclude his book with the thought – 'The probability that there are forces at work in the universe of which we have as yet scarcely an inkling is not too bizarre to entertain'.[89]

Naturally we wonder about the nature of these forces, this vigour and vitality factor. The unremitting trend towards ever greater variety and ingenuity of life forms seems to suggest that the underlying motivation behind this exuberant proliferation can be seen as the sheer joy of creation. As noted in an earlier chapter, the indisputable fact that our human products are invariably preceded by an idea in a mind suggests that nature's products are likewise preceded by an idea in a suprahuman *mind*. The obvious corollary is that our human creative urge is paralleled by a suprahuman *creative urge*. It is not unreasonable to think that our human urge to invent and create, and the satisfaction it brings us, is but a pale reflection of the higher-level Creative Urge and Satisfaction. I will return to this intriguing conjecture in a later chapter.

CHAPTER VI

THE CREATION/EVOLUTION RUMPUS

The U.S.A. monkey trials. Churchgoers in America. Newton's apple.
Weeping angels. The earth was born yesterday! Homology cuts both
ways. A variegation of viewpoints.

In recent decades a wordy and ill-tempered conflict has been raging
in the educational and scientific establishments of the U.S.A., with
both sides, Creationists and Evolutionists, accusing the other of
promulgating beliefs which are nothing but suppositions unsup-
ported by factual evidence. The Creationists claim, not without
some justification, that Evolutionary Theory is really nothing but a
suppositional hypothesis rather than a proven theory, and that in
fairness to pupils the alternative hypothesis of Creation should
receive at least equal prominence in the educational curriculum.
The Evolutionists counterclaim that Evolutionary Theory,
although once suppositional, has in the course of time become fact
just as firmly based as any other fact of science. Judging from what
we have seen in the preceding pages, it is perhaps not unfair to
suggest that this counterclaim is not altogether free from wishful
thinking.

Although the Creationists appear to have a case worthy of
thoughtful consideration, they have I think weakened it by naming
it Creation Science. They did so in an endeavour to get round the
fact that the American Constitution forbids state intervention in

religion, and prohibits the teaching of religion in public schools. Their choice of name naturally irritated the scientific community and added fuel to the flames of dispute.

The conflict first errupted into a national issue in 1925 with the famous 'monkey trial' in Dayton, Tennessee, where a young biology teacher, John Scopes, was prosecuted for breaking a law passed by the legislature of the State, under pressure by the Creationists, forbidding the teaching of evolution in its schools. The famous trials lawyer, Clarence Darrow, was retained by the American Civil Liberties Union to act as Defence Attorney for Scopes, and the three-times Presidential candidate, William Bryan, was Prosecution Attorney. The judge refused permission for expert witnesses to be called on behalf of the defence, and the jury passed a verdict of guilty on Scopes, since he had after all, violated the law. The judge sentenced Scopes to a modest fine of some $200, which was later quashed on the grounds that the jury had not been given the opportunity of agreeing the fine. Many readers will remember the film drama *Inherit The Wind*, in which Spencer Tracey played the part of Defence Attorney.

Some thirty-five years after the Scopes trial when the Tennessee law forbidding the teaching of evolution was upheld, the State of Arkansas passed a 'Balanced Treatment' law requiring that equal classroom time be allocated to teaching Creation in schools teaching Evolution. At the end of the year in which the law was passed, it was challenged by the American Civil Liberties Union at a U.S. Federal Court in Little Rock in Arkansas. After a ten-day acrimonious hearing, Judge William Overton ruled that Creation Science so called was really religion in disguise, and as such, banned from the classroom by the American Constitution. Vivid if decidely partisan accounts of the Court proceedings by both Michael Ruse and Gene Lyon can be found in Ashley Montagu's collection of essays.[59] It tickled my sense of humour to learn that after ten days spent in ridiculing the Creationists, the Evolutionists spent the last evening in a celebration which ended with communal hymn singing.

I find it a little strange that so much acrimony and denunciation

65

should have been sustained for so long in a country which prides itself on being one of the great superpowers of the modern world. Perhaps the answer is to be found in the fact that, despite – or perhaps because of – the American ban on State involvement in religion, church attendance is far greater than in this country. It is reported that fifty per cent of American youth attend church regularly, and that a third of these have strong fundamentalist leanings.[56] It is said also that the adult population is split fifty-fifty between those who accept the Adam and Eve story, and those who believe that man has evolved over millions of years, possibly with assistance from God.[56] An associated factor is undoubtedly the success of the Creationist movement in influencing the publishers of school text books to play down or delete references to evolution.[56]

The Creationists, smarting under the sting of having their claim to be a science rejected, retaliated by claiming that if creation is religious, then evolution is no less so. Needless to say, this response further enraged the scientific fraternity, adding yet more fuel to an already fierce conflagration. If only the Creationists had tried to exercise a modest degree of tact, and contented themselves with remarking that evolution itself involves faith in the unprovable, and in that sense is like religion, they might conceivably have avoided the danger of escalating an already bitter conflict.

But the Creationists are not the only ones to exacerbate! In *The Case Against Creationism*, Philip Kitcher asserts that although it is put forward as an attack on evolution, it is really an attack on the whole of science.[48] He seeks to support this view with the extraordinary assertion that, because we cannot positively guarantee the validity of Newton's Laws of Dynamics, since an 'unknown factor' (a sudden gust of wind?) might alter the trajectory of a falling apple it follows that evolutionary theory is no more unscientific than Newton's laws! It is somewhat disconcerting to find such an argument being used to support the contention that Creationism is an attack on the whole of science. It reminds me of a comment received from the Editor of the prestigious journal *Nature*, saying 'It was no more incumbent on Darwin to explain where Natural

Selection came from, than it was incumbent on Newton to explain where the Laws of Dynamics came from'. This was the reason given for rejecting an article I had submitted on the difficulty of explaining natural selection by evolutionary theory (see page 25).

Montagu prefaces his Introduction with a well-known stanza from Shakespeare's *Measure for Measure*:

> Man, proud man,
> Drest in a little brief authority,
> Most ignorant of what he's most assur'd,
> His glassy essence, like an angry ape,
> Plays such fantastic tricks before high heaven
> As make the angels weep.

Doubtless both sides in the dispute will see these lines as epitomising their opponents, thereby giving support to my view that they are equally applicable to both. Well might the angels weep!

In addition to the Creationist's provocative double claim that a) Creation is scientific, and b) Evolution is religious, they embrace several other controversial points of principle. One is their taken-for-granted assumption that Creation necessarily implies an omnipotent, omniscient Creator, and that conversely, Evolution necessarily implies the non-existence of a Creator. Another is their total disregard of the problem of reconciling the concept of a loving omnipotent Creator with the failure of the vast majority of creatures to survive the hazards of existence.

Apart from these basic points of principle, the Creationist's case is in my view further weakened by several practical points arising from their insistence on a literal interpretation of the The Book of Genesis. Chief among these points is their insistence that the earth is only a few thousand years old, in disregard of the findings of science. They support this extraordinary claim by arguing that the radiometric method of measurement used by science is unreliable because it is based on unprovable assumptions of the constancy of natural laws and phenomena. Strictly speaking, this is true, but it is a question of *degree*. Scientists can be as dogmatic and pig-headed as anyone else, but whatever their faults, they are not totally

67

incompetent technically, and it is ridiculous to think that their methods are so inept as to be incapable of distinguishing between geological ages of few thousand or a few billion years. Radiometric methods of measuring age have been used by scientists over many years, and have been continually refined and cross-checked. It has been established that the rate of radioactive atomic decay is not significantly influenced by changes in pressure or temperature. A high degree of accuracy is not claimed, but it seems unlikely that the innate errors can exceed something like fifty per cent at most. An error of anything like a million to one, as implied by the Creationists, is sheer fantasy.

The Evolution case also has its weaknesses, some of which have been discussed in earlier chapters. Probably a majority of evolutionists would agree with Julian Huxley's pronouncement that 'Darwinism removed the whole idea of God as the Creator of organisms, from the sphere of rational discussion'. Others might go further, and accept the Dawkinsian view that the idea of a Creator is refuted by our human inability to account for His origin. A minority might echo Ashley Montagu's statement that 'There is no incompatibility between belief in God and the belief that evolution is the means by which all living things have come into being'.[59] But I suspect they would, in some cases at least, echo it with more than a trace of tongue-in-cheek!

I referred right at the beginning of this book (page 3) to what must surely be the most ubiquitous of all the fallacies in the Evolutionists' case, namely the unproved *assumption* that genetic mutations are necessarily always *random* with respect to the needs and welfare of the organism in which they occur. This taken-for-granted assumption, which lies at the heart of Neo-Darwinian evolutionary theory, is nothing but supposition pure and simple, conjecture unproven and unprovable. Yet it seems to be accepted as proven fact by almost all Evolutionists. For instance, Jacque Monod opined 'Pure chance, absolutely free but blind, at the very root of the stupendous edifice of evolution . . . is today the sole conceivable hypothesis, the only one compatible with observed and tested fact'.[57]

Another widespread fallacy is to think that Neo-Darwinism has now been so thoroughly tested that it can be regarded as *fact*, not just theory. Many Evolutionists have asserted this opinion as though it were a proven fact, but it is nothing of the sort. Julian Huxley, grandson of the famous Thomas Huxley, 'Darwin's Bulldog', asserted bluntly 'The first point to make about Darwin's theory is that it is no longer a theory, but a fact'.[35] Ashley Montagu asserts firmly 'Evolution is a fact, not a theory. It was once a theory, but today it is probably the best authenticated actuality known to science'.[59] The same goes for Richard Dawkins' frequent assertions that Darwinian theory is the *only* theory capable of explaining life.

A further widespread fallacy in the Evolutionist case is the assumption that homology, the use of similiar structures in different organisms, is an indication of common ancestry, and hence provides strong evidence for evolution. A frequently-quoted example is the marked similarity between the forelimbs of different animals such as lizard, eagle, bat, man, etc. (see Figure 6). A still more striking example is shown in Figure 7, which is a reproduction of a 16th century drawing of the skeletons of bird and man. A very different example is given by Dawkins – that of the genetic code, which is universal throughout nature. He regards this as 'near-conclusive proof that all organisms are descended from a common ancestor'.[19/270] Maybe it is, but how does this prove evolution?

It is quite true that homology *could* be an indication of common ancestry, but what the Evolutionists overlook is that it could equally well be an indication of common design, or creation by a common source. I find it hard to understand why the Creationist camp do not make use of this irrefutable argument. Perhaps it is because of their own assumption that creation is necessarily the work of an omnipotent God, Who would not be likely to stoop to the lazy expedient of utilising common features for different purposes, but would design every organism in the way best suited to its needs. More of this anon.

Yet another Evolutionist fallacy is their universal assumption that if a biological feature can be shown to be advantageous, then that is

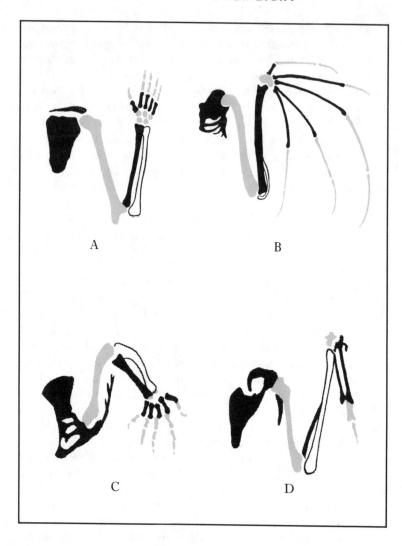

Figure 6   The same bones from the arm of a man (A), a bat (B), a lizard (C) and an eagle (D) are here given the same colour to show the common structural plan. (Redrawn after J. Huxley and taken from *The History of Man*, by Gustav Schenk.)

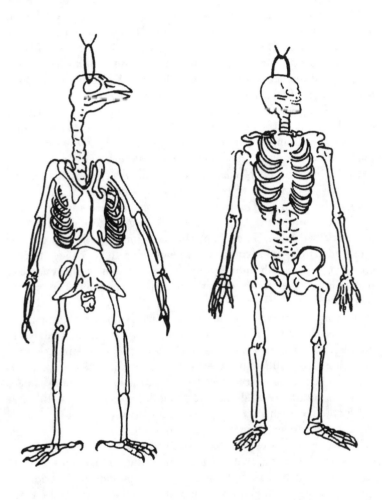

Figure 7   Reproduced from *The History of Man*, Gustav Schenk. Copyright 1961 by Belser Verlag, Stuttgart, Germany.

clear evidence that it must have evolved by the processes of the natural selection of advantageous variations. Again, they overlook the fact that it could equally well be seen as evidence of intelligent design. Why do they overlook it? It seems to me that it can only be because of a naive, but deeply ingrained, belief that the whole idea of God is quite untenable to any intelligent person with his feet on the ground and his head *not* in the clouds. If any other explanation is *possible*, then, they think, it is greatly to be preferred.

One more source of dispute is the rarity of mutations, which we have already noted. The Evolutionist camp maintains that this point is irrelevant, saying that it is not the frequency of mutations per gene that matters, but the frequency per population. This may sound sensible, but I find it beside the point, which is simply that genetic mutations or copying errors *are* very rare *relative to the number of error-free copyings.** Quoting Dawkins again, he compares mutations with typing errors, which a good typist can keep down to only one error per page. He explains that to compete with the very low rate of genetic errors, typing errors would have to be reduced to only one error in several hundred pages, or less than one wrong character per million correct ones. It is the *relative* proportion of mutations that matters, not the absolute numbers.

Incidentally, it is interesting to note that Kitcher cites a figure of about ten billion mutations per generation for the present world population of Homo sapiens, which at a rough guess implies a total of at least 100 billion mutations during the last 25,000 years. It seems to be generally accepted that the physiology of Homo sapiens has changed little, if at all, in that period, so it seems that in this case at least, the overwhelming majority of mutations have had very little effect on the organism in which they occurred.

There are other evolutionary problems which we have already discussed, including that of explaining the sudden outbursts of speciation which interrupt relatively long periods of inaction, to make good the continual losses due to extinctions. And there is the problem of how natural selection can act upon an advantageous

---

* Hitchings quotes a figure of once per 10 million cell divisions.[38]

feature in the interim stages before it is sufficiently developed to function properly. There is also the problem of correlating the evolution of functionally cooperating elements of a complex biological mechanism.

So far I have talked only of the American brand of Creationism, but most of what I have said is equally applicable to their British equivalent, the Creation Science Movement.[14] This group holds to the same principle of a strictly literal interpretation of Genesis, including an earth age of a few thousand years, a six-day period of Divine Creation, Adam and Eve, the Fall, the Flood, Noah's Ark, etc. They seem to be less influential than their American counterpart, presumably because our clergy are less intolerant in their approach to evolution, and in any case, church attendance in this country is very much lower than in the U.S.A.

It is only fair to point out that there are other forms of Creationism, and other protest movements with more liberal views, such as the Biblical Creation Society, founded in this country in 1976.[6] There is also a Research Scientists Christian Fellowship, with broadly similiar views.[5] These movements have dropped the demand for a literal reading of Genesis, retaining only the 'Fall' of mankind through the Adam-and-Eve sin of disobedience, and the consequent redemption through the sacrifice of Christ. I find it somewhat ironic that it should be the *Biblical* Creation Society that adopts a non-literal approach to Bible reading, and the Creation *Science* Movement that adopts a decidedly unscientific approach to creation, but no matter.

What is very noticeable about these various groups is their unrelenting internal warfare. Man seems to have a psychological penchant for seeking out the faults of his fellows, combined with a marked aversion to finding common ground with them. This negative characteristic of human nature is particularly prominent among opposing politicians, but is also very evident among scientists and philosophers. In a little book hailed by Prof. Berry as one of the two most important British books on Creationism, David Watson lambasts Berry as heartily as he lambasts the Evolutionists.[95] He accuses Berry of 'clutching at every straw that promises hope of survival of Darwinism', and roundly condemns him for citing Phillip Gosse, who in 1857 published a book asserting that God created rocks with fossils already in them in order to give the *appearance* of age. Watson asserts that this is irrelevant to the modern debate, but I should have thought it is still very relevant. He concludes his attack on Berry by saying that 'It is indeed regrettable that one so highly gifted should waste his talents defending the pagan philosophy [of evolution]'.

For a little light relief, it is noteworthy that the primary feature of Gosse's book was a dissertation on the question of whether or not Adam had a navel! Not being born of woman, he did not need one, but nevertheless God created him with one in order to save him embarrassment at being different to all his descendants, Gosse decided. Watson refers to 'poor Phillip Gosse', but I wonder whether perhaps Gosse's book was really meant as a leg-pull, and thus had the last laugh!

Back to reality! What seems to have upset Watson most about Berry's book is its assertion that the main-spring of American Creationism is simply fear that the challenge of evolution may cause irreparable damage to the accepted framework of religious belief, and open a Pandora's box of uncontrolled social behaviour. Berry claims that this fear produces 'stunted Christians' incapable of mature thought, and encourages a ghetto mentality in the churches. It seems to me that there is plenty of sense in these words. Whilst I cannot accept the 'Fundamentalist' brand of Creationism, I share their concern for the ill-effects of undiluted orthodox evolutionary theory on social behaviour and moral values. It seems a pity that Watson could not have said the same for Berry's book.[95]

So much for the on-going creation versus evolution rumpus. It doesn't say much for man's powers of rational, impartial thinking, and seems to bear out what I said in the Preface about evolution being judged more by personal preconceptions and predilections than by logic.

As well as the two main groups of Creationists we have discussed above, there are a variety of other views around, some of which are indicated in the table below. Needless to say, each group think that they are right, and all the others wrong!

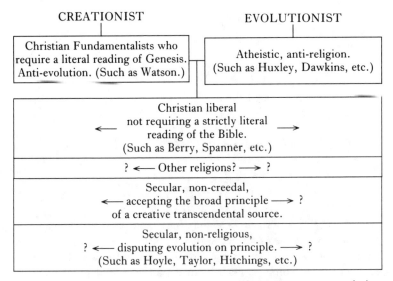

CREATIONIST   EVOLUTIONIST

CREATIONIST		EVOLUTIONIST
Christian Fundamentalists who require a literal reading of Genesis. Anti-evolution. (Such as Watson.)		Atheistic, anti-religion. (Such as Huxley, Dawkins, etc.)
Christian liberal not requiring a strictly literal reading of the Bible. ← (Such as Berry, Spanner, etc.) →		
? ← Other religions? → ?		
Secular, non-creedal, ← accepting the broad principle → ? of a creative transcendental source.		
Secular, non-religious, ? ← disputing evolution on principle. → ? (Such as Hoyle, Taylor, Hitchings, etc.)		

Note, this table is schematic only, without pretence to being comprehensive or absolute.

CHAPTER VII

TAKING STOCK

The unresolved quandary. Preconceptions and misconceptions.

The reader who has persevered so far may well begin to wonder where it is all leading, so let's pause a moment, and take stock of the situation. We have examined in brief outline two possible explanations of the origin of the tremendous variety of the world of nature, a) it is the outcome of Darwinian evolution based on the natural selection of fortuitous variations, or b) it was created by an omnipotent Creator. Both these two alternatives contain major problems which have to be resolved if either is to be acceptable to thinking people in our time.

The more closely the hypothesis of Evolution is examined, the more intractable are its problems found to be. Using the admittedly far-fetched, but I think not altogether unreasonable analogy of typing, it is like expecting a faulty document to be improved by the accumulation of typing errors in repeated copyings, with a conscientious editor retaining any errors which show a slight improvement, and rejecting all the others. And we noted in passing that something over *100 billion* mutations during the last 25,000 years of history has not had any significant effect on human physiology. Richard Dawkins has attempted a spirited defence of Darwinism by postulating a highly efficient form of cumulative selection, but although providing a dramatic computer demonstration, this is found on careful

76

examination to be quite inapplicable to real life conditions. And Dawkins himself has shown that the alternative of sequential selection is debarred by an astronomically high number of improbabilities.

The alternative hypothesis of Creation as promulgated in the U.S.A., also poses major problems which must make it unacceptable to most people in this scientifically oriented materialistic age. Apart from its insistence on a literal reading of the Christian Bible, it postulates a transcendental Source of Creation, an omnipotent loving Divinity which few people can reconcile with the unmerited suffering and distress, the waste and inefficiency, the failed experiments and false starts, of the world of nature.

So with the two main contenders for the title of explaining the world of nature found wanting, we seem to be left in an unresolvable quandary. Yet there has to *be* an answer, presumably something other than either of the two main contestants. I believe it lies, strangely enough, in what might be broadly described as an amalgam or synthesis of the two, which has been overlooked only because of the antagonistic, intolerant reactions of each side to the other's views. Both are so deeply enmeshed in their own intellectual edifice of sectarian doctrine as to be totally incapable of visualising, let alone seeking, a constructive amalgam of the two opposing views.

It is difficult to achieve an objective assessment of a new theory which appears to contravene some of the conscious and unconscious beliefs and preconceptions which upbringing and education have imposed on most people without their knowledge or consent. Many of these preconceptions have already been mentioned in the preceding pages, but it may perhaps be helpful to recapitulate briefly, adding one or two more not previously dealt with:

1) *The educational establishment, particularly at university level, teaches only that which is generally validated by the scientific establishment. Evolutionary theory is accepted as a valid branch of science.*

Comment. This widespread assumption sounds reasonable, but can be misleading if taken too seriously. The educational system is sluggish in its response to changes of paradigm in the professional disciplines on which it is based. The fact that something has been taught for generations is no guarantee of its validity, and this is just as applicable to science as to religion, which only a small minority feel able to accept without question these days.

2) *All the phenomena of nature can be explained in physical terms. The concept of a non-physical spiritual realm is a human invention. Science has exposed religion as an out-dated superstition. Mind does not exist in its own right, it is simply the effect of brain activity. Dualistic explanations are a counsel of intellectual bankruptcy. The objective physical world is the only reality.*

Comment. We noted in Chapter I that there are sound logical reasons for rejecting these materialistic views. Matter itself is in essence immaterial, nothing but a vast concurrence of interacting energy fields. The *seemingly* real and solid world revealed by our senses is strictly speaking a mental construct evoked by the brain activity resulting from the input of signals from the sensory organs. Our subjective experience cannot be both the cause and the effect of brain activity; emotions and perceptions are in the mind, not the brain. All man-made products originate as an *idea* in a mind, and there is no *a priori* reason to think that this principle is not equally applicable to nature's products. Colour is one example of the many things that cannot be explained in purely physical terms; it is a mental sensation devoid of objective physical existence. Many of the greatest scientists have expressed their belief in a non-physical realm of existence.

3) *One of the things which makes it hard to appreciate the credibility of evolution is our human difficulty of grasping the immensity of geological time. We are used to thinking in terms of decades and centuries, and even millennia, but it is extremely difficult to envisage periods of hundreds of millions of years involved in evolutionary processes.*

Comment. This is quite true, but beside the point. The basic factor in evolution is not so much the length of time available, as the outweighing of the very occasional beneficial variation by the overwhelmingly more numerous harmful or neutral variations.

4) *The only internal cause of structural variations in embryos (as distinct from external causes in its environment) is genetic mutation. And the only known external cause of genetic mutations (as distinct from internal causes such as recombination of chromosonal sections during meiosis) is radiation and chemical mutagens.*

Comment. There is no *a priori* reason why genes and embryos should not be affected by non-physical influences. As we saw in Chapter I, emotions and volition are in the mind, not the brain, and there can be no reason to think that genes and embryos can not be affected by non-physical factors. The fact that science knows nothing of the non-physical realm does not imply that no such realm exists. Science is concerned not with the qualitative non-physical realm of subjective realities such as consciousness, sensation, emotion, volition, but only with the quantitative realm of the 'objective' physical world.

5) *Natural selection is the primary feature of Darwinism, and selection is not a chance process. It is therefore incorrect to regard evolution as a chance process.*

Comment. This argument is fallacious. Selection is not an active process; there is no extraneous selecting agency in operation in nature. Selection is simply an outcome of the imperative will to live and reproduce which is innate in *all* life, from the most primitive to the most sophisticated. Obviously a feature which is common to *all* life cannot originate in variations in any particular form of life.

6) *Homology between species is widespread, and strongly suggests common ancestry, which is best explained by evolution. Special creation is an unnecessary hypothesis.*

Comment. Common ancestry can equally well be regarded as evidence of design by a common source.

7) *Biological organisms are subject to a continued flux of small variations, and any of these which prove advantageous are naturally selected by the struggle to survive and the will to live,*

and incorporated in the organism. Evolution is dependent on, and demonstrated by, the presence of advantageous features. If it can be shown that an existing feature is advantageous, that is clear evidence that it evolved.

Comment. The presence of advantageous features can equally well be regarded as evidence of design by an intelligent source.

8) *The evolution of even the most complex structure (such as the eye) becomes quite feasible if one postulates a sufficient number of finely-graded intermediate steps each providing some slight advantage.*

Comment. Functionally interacting elements of a biological structure must come into existence simultaneously or concurrently if it is to function properly. It is therefore highly unlikely that they can evolve in a series of discrete non-sequential steps. This principle must apply at some stage, even if the structure in question starts off by fulfilling a different function to its final one.

9) *The production of new species is simply the automatic effect of long-continued natural selection of advantageous variations. Species become well adapted to their current environment, and their extinction is therefore a great puzzle.*

Comment. Advantageous variations are overwhelmingly outnumbered by harmful or neutral variations. It follows that the overall effect of variations is more likely to be a reduction in the number of species, rather than a proliferation. The real puzzle becomes speciation, not extinction.

10) *The many design imperfections in nature are incompatible with the postulate of an omnipotent creator.*

Comment. The postulate of design in nature does not, in itself, imply an omnipotent source of design and creation.

11) *Evolution is not inimical to religion. There is no incompatibility between a belief in God and a belief that evolution is the means by which living organisms came into being.*

Comment. This is a matter of opinion. To the ordinary man and woman, and to the ordinary student, the assertion that life arose from random variations seems equivalent to asserting that religion is an out-dated superstition.

12) *It is pointless to explain our existence, or the existence of the universe, in terms of a transcendental source which is itself inexplicable.*

Comment. This is a sophism, a paralogism, a non-argument. Things do not become impossible merely because our little human minds are incapable of understanding them. The transcendental is by definition beyond our human understanding. Man can no more explain that which is beyond his understanding than an ant can explain a man.

13) *The hypothesis of creation implies the action of a deity who created the universe and its contents. The Bible is the inspired record of the creative activities of the Creator.*

Comment. The hypothesis of Creation does not in itself imply any particular source of creation, apart from its transcendence of human abilities. And the Christian Bible was obviously written by human hands, which cannot be infallible. It is perfectly reasonable to regard the Bible as allegorical rather than factual. After all, Jesus himself spoke in parable or allegory.

CHAPTER VIII

ORIGINS

The awesome universe. The hot big bang. Where has all the energy gone? Bohm and the Implicate Order. Fragmentation. Spontaneous generation revived?

An unavoidable problem inhering in any discussion of creation (in contradistinction to evolution) lies in our human difficulty of visualising a *source* of creation. Most people take it for granted that God is the creative source but, as noted on the previous page, the hypothesis of creation does not in itself imply any particular source of creation, apart from the fact that it must completely transcend any possible human ability.

Over the centuries that little word *God* has gathered unto itself a deeply entrenched connotation of personhood, of 'God the Father'. Deeply immured as we all are in our individual sense of being an embodied person, it is difficult to break free from this instinctive anthropomorphic concept of God. Judging from the wording in *The Blind Watchmaker*, Dawkins is obviously thinking in these terms when he refers to a supernatural designer, a pre-existent Being of prodigious intelligence and complexity, capable not only of designing something as sophisticated as the genetic system with the universal DNA code, but also of such 'advanced functions' as listening to prayer and forgiving sins.[19/141]

In my own experience it is not until one manages to acquire at least a vague glimpse of the awesome magnitude of the universe and its problems, that one begins to realise the sheer incongruity of any sort of anthropomorphic concept as the source of it all. This is a difficult issue of great import, so let's consider it more fully.

Imagine a 600 gallon tank, filled not with oil, but with fine table salt packing fifteen million grains in a tea-cup. The tank would hold some 200 billion grains of salt, and this is roughly the number of stars in our galaxy.[37] There are hundreds, perhaps thousands of billions of galaxies in the universe, so in order to represent the whole universe you would need something like ten further tanks *for every single one of the 200 billion grains of sand in the first tank*! If this is too difficult to take in, then alternatively visualise a gargantuan canal 40,000 kilometres long (enough to encircle the earth), several kilometres wide, and fifty metres deep (about the height of Nelson's Column). It would take a fast car about a fortnight of non-stop driving to travel the length of this canal. Now fill the canal with fine powdery sand of the same grain size as table salt, and you have the number of stars in the universe. Alternatively, use a gigantic steel balloon of about 12 kilometres diameter! These simulations are not easy to visualise, but they may serve to give some slight impression of the stupendous immensity of the universe, not forgetting that a large proportion of the septillions of stars will be likely to have a planetary system not unlike our own.

Throughout the main period of galaxy formation of perhaps a billion years, stars must have been coming into existence at the incredible rate of *millions* every *second*! Most readers will probably know that our sun is a fairly average to middling second-generation star.

In the actual universe the stars are spaced out at vast distances apart, not tightly packed together as in our salt tanks. Keeping to the same scale of roughly 100 billion to 1, each sand grain would be spaced about *ten kilometres* from its nearest neighbour, and the whole micro-universe of sand grains would be around twenty billion kilometres across. The earth would be an invisible microscopic speck about two-and-a-half microns in diameter, say one thirtieth of the thickness of a human hair.

Distances in the actual universe are so vast that they are usually measured in light-years. Light travels at a velocity of 300,000 kilometres per second, which means that it can travel a distance equal to the circumference of the earth in one seventh of a second, literally the blink of an eye. The universe is estimated to be something like *ten billion light-years* across.

The question which inevitably springs to mind is, where did all this inconceivable immensity come from? Most readers will probably be aware that science finds the universe to be expanding, which obviously means that it must have been smaller in the past. The rate of expansion has been determined with reasonable accuracy, and suggests that the universe must have started billions of years ago in an unimaginably compressed condition, a sort of 'primordial egg' of virtually infinite density and temperature. At time zero, this exploded in an inconceivably violent Hot Big Bang to form a primordial fireball of radiant energy, far too hot to condense into atoms of matter. After about one million years, the fireball had expanded to some billions of billions of kilometres across, and the temperature had dropped to a mere few thousand degrees, allowing the formation of a white-hot gaseous mixture of stabilised hydrogen and helium atoms, which over the next hundreds of millions of years condensed out into the untold septillions of stars mentioned above.[82,33]

This cataclysmic event was critically dependent on a number of factors. If the rate of expansion of the fireball had been very slightly slower, it would have collapsed before matter started to condense out into hydrogen and helium nuclei; and if it had been slightly faster, expansion would have continued past the stage where gravitational forces could have caused the hot gases to condense into atoms of matter.[49,53,82] Other critical factors were the relative masses and charges of the subatomic particles, and the values of natural constants such as the gravitational force, the electromagnetic force, and the nuclear force.

Is it remotely conceivable that all these critical values just happened by a fluke of luck to be exactly what was required to produce a universe? Is it sensible to think that the primordial egg was there without cause or source? Was it pure luck that caused it to be surrounded by an empty void of nothingness that it could expand into when it happened to explode in the Big Bang?

And in any case, how was it *able* to explode – its virtually infinite density would have made it a sort of super-blackhole from which *nothing*, not even the massless photons of light, can escape, due to the enormous gravitational attraction. So how was it able to release its contents, whatever form they took? The only answer I can see is that the *thermal energy* corresponding to its near-infinite temperature must have been great enough to overcome the enormous gravitational attraction; but where did this thermal energy come from? One of the basic axioms of science is 'the conservation of energy', meaning that the total quantity of energy is constant, that is, it can neither be created nor destroyed, but can only change from one form to another. So I repeat, what was the *source* of the thermal energy needed to overcome the gravitational pull of the primordial egg or super-blackhole?*

Despite the inability of science to answer these basic questions of principle, it seems that scientists will go to any lengths to avoid accepting the possibility, let alone the probability, of the intervention in nature of any sort of transcendental supraphysical cause outside the scope of physical science. For instance, the physicist Heinz Pagel asserts that the total energy of the universe would be *zero* if it had about ten times *more* mass, meaning that it would have required no energy for its creation![70] He bases this extraordinary assertion on the assumption that the total energy is obtained by *subtracting* the potential energy of the expanding galaxies from the total mass energy of the matter particles. He claims that the 'negative' potential energy is about ten times greater than the 'positive' mass energy, and that if they were identical this would give the zero total energy condition. He goes on to opine that there is a tiny quantum probability that a vacuum will 'convert itself' into a Big Bang explosion, and that however remote the probability may be, 'it will certainly happen sometime'. He concludes that the universe is 'a creation by the God that plays dice', which sounds like a reference to Einstein's famous objection to the Uncertainty Principle.

---

* See Postscript for further discussion.

Stephen Hawking supports this 'zero total energy' hypothesis,[34] on the same broad grounds that the 'negative' potential energy should be subtracted from the 'positive' mass energy, although unlike Pagel he asserts that they are equal *now*, and thus balance out already. And he reaches a negative view of the possibility of God, by an alternative route, explaining that if time is interpreted as 'imaginary time' measured by imaginary numbers such as the square root of minus 1, then space and time can be seen as an unbounded space-time continuum without beginning or end. He then makes the point that whilst it may not be unreasonable to postulate a creator of a universe that had a beginning, you can hardly do so for a universe that had no beginning. He considers imaginary time to be just as real as normal time, or at least just as valid a concept.

Speaking as an admitted amateur, unversed in manipulating abstract mathematics, I find difficulty in understanding the argument that the gravitational potential energy of the spaced-apart galaxies is a negative quantity. Energy is a non-directional scalar quantity, not a directional vector quantity. The expression 'negative energy' is to my mind a contradiction in terms. As I see it, immediately after the Big Bang the energy involved was primarily kinetic, which is in process of becoming potential energy as the rate of expansion slows down under the influence of gravitational attraction. The total of the diminishing kinetic energy plus the increasing potential energy remains constant. To find the total energy of the universe, we add to this combination of kinetic and potential energy, the rest-mass energy of the matter particles, and the thermal energy.*

It seems to me that what these two astrophysicists have really demonstrated is not so much the energy characteristics of the universe, as the overwhelming stranglehold of crystallised dogma. Despite a massive 10 to 1 disparity of energy estimates, both parties seem to think that they have advanced a powerful argument against the possibility of some sort of transcendental supraphysical influence controlling the origin and continued existence of the universe. For

---

* See Postscript for further discussion.

generations the scientific establishment has been unshakeably persuaded that *everything* in nature can be accounted for in terms of Darwinian principles of an accumulation of advantageous random variations. This outlook has become a sort of congenital habit of thought, a philosophy of life which brooks no discussion.[51] Any theories which show promise of supporting it are eagerly pounced upon and uncritically accepted without serious examination or discussion – or so it seems to me anyway

A very different, and I think more profound, view of these great cosmic issues has been advanced by the distinguished physicist Prof. David Bohm.[8] I quote:

Current quantum field theory implies that what appears to be empty space contains an immense 'zero point energy', coming from all the quantum fields that are contained in this space. Matter is then a relatively small wave or disturbance on top of this 'ocean' of energy. Using reasonable assumptions, *the energy of one cubic centimetre of space is far greater than would be available from the nuclear disintegration of all the matter in the known universe!* Matter is therefore a 'small ripple' on this ocean of energy. [my italics]

It is relevant to note that, according to his fascinating recent book,[18] John Davidson observes that another physicist, J. A. Wheeler, made much the same point back in 1962.

The basis of Prof. Bohm's thesis is his famous Implicate Order hypothesis, which he illustrates with a simple mechanical analogy using two concentric cylinders, one fixed, one rotatable, with an annular gap between them. This space is filled with a viscous liquid such as treacle or glycerine, and an ink drop is inserted into this viscous liquid. When one cylinder is slowly rotated, the ink drop becomes drawn out into a circumferential line, which eventually becomes so fine as to be invisible, so that the ink drop is 'enfolded' in the viscous fluid. If now the rotation is reversed, the invisible line becomes reconstituted into its original drop form. Additional ink drops can be inserted one by one as each preceding drop becomes enfolded, the rotation being repeated for each new drop. Reverse rotation now causes the drops to re-appear in reverse order and become re-enfolded in the reverse direction. If this sequence can be speeded up, the re-appearing drops give the impression of a continuously moving spot appearing out of nowhere.

The condition where the ink drops are enfolded in the viscous fluid represents the Implicate Order, and the condition where they have re-appeared represents an Explicate Order of manifested objects. Another analogy can be drawn from television or radio, where the visual and audio information is enfolded in the carrier wave put out by the transmitter, and is explicated or made manifest by the receiving set. A further analogy is provided by the hologram, where a visually indecipherable optical-interference image on photographic film is formed by a combination of reflected and direct laser light, and can be visually reconstituted by viewing with laser light. If a small part of the image is thus viewed, the whole object is revealed, so that it can be said that in principle every part of the hologram enfolds the original object.

Bohm points out that as human knowledge proliferates, it inevitably becomes fragmented into specialised compartments, each tending to see itself as *separate* rather than part of a unified whole. When this ever-increasing degree of specialisation is compounded with the almost universal habit of equating our thought patterns and theories with reality, with the 'real world as it is', then the fragmentation effect is reinforced, leading to a false and restricted view of reality which tends to encourage inter-group misunderstanding and conflict. We approach nature with limited, and more or less fixed, habits of thought endlessly confirmed.

As Bohm observes, orthodox physics is based on a mechanistic reductionist approach, with separate objects spacially apart, as in a machine. This view sees the world as a collection of building blocks, of electrons, atoms, molecules, etc. Bohm suggests that a closer approach to reality can be achieved by thinking in terms of an Implicate Order of pure undifferentiated energy in which everything is enfolded or embedded, and becomes explicate or objectified by the act of conscious attention. An electron can be seen as a tightly-spaced sequence of explications, like the viscous-fluid analogy of moving ink-drops suddenly appearing out of nothing. The almost infinite energy of the vacuum is the source of the Implicate Order in which everything is enfolded. Bohm postulates a (possibly infinite) hierarchy of Implicate and Superimplicate Orders in which *every-thing*, including life, mind, and consciousness, is enfolded. A high level in this hierarchy may be the source of a sort of 'protointelligence' which underlies all the manifest expressions of life throughout the vast universe.

The current approach to biology and evolution treats the Explicate order as primary, and assumes that everything in nature can be accounted for in terms of DNA molecules, cells, etc. It holds that life arose from the interactions of random molecular combinations leading to ever more complex organisms. Whilst this approach has been fruitful in uncovering much of the detailed working of the natural world, it cannot explain the presence of life itself, of mind and consciousness and volition. This can only be accounted for in terms of a deeper reality which sees life, mind, and consciousness as an expression of a universal Implicate Order in which *everything* is enfolded.

Bohm suggests that the problems involved in the coordinated development of all the new biological structures necessary to ensure the successful operation of a new feature such as flight, can be accounted for by assuming a period of 'free play' of the genetic system, which encourages the concurrent formation of totalities of structures emerging from subtle levels of Implicate Order under the influence of 'feedback' from one level to another, with the postulated protointelligence exercising overall control. This free-play hypothesis could also provide an explanation of the periodic outbursts of speciation activity mentioned on page 62.

Whilst the foregoing brief outline cannot do justice to the grandeur of Bohm's hypothesis of the Implicate Orders of the universe, it may perhaps serve to give those not already acquainted with it, a preliminary glimpse of the impressive explanatory powers it provides for some of the deep mysteries of life which orthodox science is quite unable to explain and usually ignores or dismisses as heresy or superstition.

A closely similar philosophy is held by John Davidson mentioned above.[18] Although he approaches the subject from the other end of the spectrum, so to speak, he arrives at the same broad conclusion that so called empty space, far from being empty, is in fact brimming with enormous energies which are the basic source of all matter and all aspects of life in the vast universe. Interestingly, he also shares the view that, since science is a product of human individuals with human emotions and prejudices, it is natural and indeed inevitable that new ideas which conflict with long-standing habitual patterns of thought and belief, will be rejected. Apart from the philosophical agreement with Bohm, Davidson's book also describes a number of practical attempts currently in being, to apply the 'zero-point' hidden energy of the vacuum plenum to human needs. I find it a fascinating book, and can recommend it to those who may perhaps find the more deeply scientific background of Bohm's books a little off-putting.

One of Davidson's points is particularly relevant to the issues discussed in the present book. As he observes, science offers no explanation of how it is that the atom is normally everlasting, apart from the radioactive decay of some unstable atoms. One of the basic tenets of science is that perpetual motion is an impossibility, the reason being that motion of any sort necessarily involves friction, and the energy absorbed in overcoming friction has to be supplied by some external source if the motion is to continue indefinitely. An atom comprises electrons circulating at very high speed around or about a central nucleus. An electron has a negative electric charge, and another of the basic tenets of science is that a moving charge dissipates energy in the form of eddy currents or magnetic induction, or perhaps interaction with other electromagnetic fields. So where does the energy absorbed in these electrical losses come from? We can go further, and ask what is the source of the energy which is of the essence of the electrons themselves? (page 19) All science tells us is that this energy is just there, indestructible, inexhaustible, everlasting. As I see it, the only conceivable source of this eternal energy must be the hidden 'zero point energy' of the so-called vacuum.

So much, then, for the 'zero total energy of the universe' syndrome.

Another assumption of the inveterate evolutionist is that, despite the generally accepted principle that life can only arise from other life, and not from inert matter, as established by men like Pasteur and Lister in the 19th century, life on earth arose from the interactions of accidental groupings of molecules. Countless man-hours have been devoted to laboratory attempts to create life, but all that has been achieved is the creation of certain pre-biotic organic molecules, such as amino acids, purines and pyrimidines that are essential to life as we know it. This is a far cry from creating even the most elementary form of self-replicating life. Indeed, it seems to me that the claim that these findings can be seen as evidence that life originated spontaneously on earth is about as far-fetched as the claim that the discovery of metal ores in the earth's crust can be seen as evidence that nails, rivets and pins, evolved by virtue of the interactions of random combinations of these raw materials. If the universe of physical matter cannot have come into existence spontaneously of its own accord, how then could the far more complex world of life have arisen spontaneously without outside assistance?

A thoughtful book by an American author throws some dramatic light on the immense problems involved in considering the possibility of the spontaneous generation of life from inanimate matter. The book is unusual in that it attempts to present a fair-minded picture of the pros and cons of evolution and creation, leaving it to the reader to choose between them. It goes into considerable detail, with support from experts in both camps. I should perhaps add that the book is not available in this country, but can be orderd directly from the American publishers on VISA account.[98] I will endeavour to outline a few of the many points it discusses:

The haemoglobin number of 10^{190} (1 followed by 190 zero's) which Dawkins instanced as the impossibly high odds against the spontaneous occurrence of just one chain of the folded four-chain haemoglobin molecule, becomes utterly insignificant when compared with the odds of $10^{167,000}$ to 1 against the spontaneous origin of all the proteins and DNA involved in the smallest self-replicating organism. A factor influencing the calculation of this enormous number is the dependence of DNA on proteins which it alone can produce; proteins are dependent on DNA for their production, yet DNA cannot form in the absence of proteins. Thus the only answer to this conundrum must be that DNA and protein evolved simultaneously, requiring that their probabilities be multiplied together.

The Evolutionist camp dispute the validity of this calculation, on the grounds that chemical bonds and combinations are not always entirely random, but are constrained to follow predestined paths determined by their atomic and molecular characteristics. But this 'chemical bias' objection raises a further problem, namely that of how it came about that the chemical characteristics of the constituents of proteins and DNA happen to be favourable rather than unfavourable to the growth of living organisms. Was it just a lucky fluke of fortune, and if so what was its probability? Or was it the outcome of intervention by an intelligent source? And in any case, assuming it did happen, would it be likely to cause a significant reduction in the calculated odds of $10^{167,000}$? This figure is so inconceivably enormous that even if it were to be reduced a billion billion-fold, it would hardly be dented. $10^{167,000}$ divided by a billion billion, i.e. 10^{18}, is $10^{166,982}$, an insignificant reduction for all practical purposes.

A further point is that even if, for the sake of the argument, one concedes the possibility of the simultaneous evolution of mutually-dependent complex macromolecules, how did the DNA molecules arrange themselves into a coded language providing *information* for the building of organisms? It is an undeniable fact that information cannot arise spontaneously from random molecular combinations; it can arise *only* from the intervention of an intelligent agent. And random rearrangement of a code devised by an intelligent source cannot increase the information content, it can only degrade it.

When all is said and done, it seems that the heart of the

controversy lies in the unshakeable conviction on the part of the Evolutionists that, whatever the improbabilities and difficulties may or may not be, at least evolution has the merit of being less incredible than creation. This conviction is presumably based on what they see as the sheer absurdity of the creation myths of the Scriptures, embracing the 'fairy tales' of Noah's Ark, Adam and Eve, the Garden of Eden, etc. Allied to this is a determination to never again fall into the trap of earlier days when any phenomenon not explicable by contemporary science was brushed aside as the outcome of Divine intervention. This trap undoubtedly impeded the advance of science, and was overcome only by 'heretical' free-thinkers who refused to bow down to ecclesiastical authority. The Creationists, on the other hand, regarded evolution as an unforgivable denial of the divinely-inspired 'Word of God'. What is at issue is not so much the validity of the concept of evolution, but rather an unresolvable radical conflict of opinion between the protagonists involved in the dispute.

Before closing this brief review of the book, I should add that its aim of impartial presentation of opposing views fails in at least one respect, namely its discussion of earth age, where only the case for a young age of a few thousand years is presented. Nevertheless, this said, it is a stimulating book which I can recommend to those wishing to delve deeper into the problems of the origin of life.

Another American book I can recommend unreservedly to readers, especially those of the rising generation, is William Fix's *The Bone Peddlers*.[102] This is without exaggeration the most informative book on evolution that I have yet come across. Another one, quite as good, is Wesson's *Beyond Natural Selection*.[105] It provides, in scholarly yet eminently readable form, an open minded and attractively frank survey of the fervently partisan approach characteristic of the evolutionary Establishments in both the U.S.A. and the U.K.

The first part of the book deals with the vexed question of man's descent from the apes, through a chain ending in Homo habilis, Homo erectus, and Neanderthal. This alleged chain, which paleoanthropologists have been promulgating for decades with almost evangelical fervour, has been thrown into considerable doubt by Richard

Leakey's discovery of fossil skull '1470', which, although far more human-looking than Neanderthal, predates him by one or two million years. Neanderthal remained static for 40,000 years, a most unhuman-like characteristic, and Homo erectus was static for a million years. For anyone interested in the genesis of Homo sapiens, this book is a must.*

Following this eye-opening introduction, the book proceeds to discuss many other basic aspects of evolutionary theory, with fascinating excursions into matters such as the following:

> Primeval earth conditions, where the 'primitive soup' postulated by experimenters such as Stanley Miller is not substantiated by the sedimentary deposits in the earth's crust.

> The phenomenon known to biologists as 'Deferred Replacement', meaning the numerous cases where new species emerge in a particular evolutionary niche long after the previous inhabitants have become extinct.

> The problems and misunderstanding arising from radiometric dating methods, with some validation from tree-ring dating techniques.

> The fallacy of assuming that homologous structures prove evolution because similar gene complexes are involved, whereas experience has shown this assumption is unfounded in fact.

> Regulator genes postulated by biologists to account for embryonic development by switching parts of the genetic code *on* or *off* at appropriate stages of development, raise more problems than they solve; for example, what regulates the regulators and tells them when to operate, and in which direction? Despite extensive search, no evidence for these postulated regulator genes has been discovered. And experimental tissue grafting work on frog eggs and developing tadpoles shows that something beyond automatic gene regulation is involved in embryonic development. For instance, if a limb bud is removed and a tail bud grafted in its place, then the tail bud becomes converted into a limb. And if the tissues in a developing frog egg are transposed by cutting and

---

* A more exhaustive discussion is provided by Roger Lewin.[104]

grafting, then material that would have become skin is converted into a spinal cord, and vice versa.

Plant and animal breeders have repeatedly found that there seems to be a definite limit to the extent of variation which can be obtained by selecting for desired characteristics. And there is a general tendency for a modified species to gradually revert to the species norm or average.

The sheer absurdity of thinking that in a vast universe with an infinite variety of life, we are limited to just two possible explanations, either miraculous creation by Divine fiat, or evolution by the automatic adoption of favourable mutations.

The equal absurdity of thinking that accidental mutations can provide increased complexity and information content.

In recent decades, the existence of a non-physical realm has been firmly established by the work of experienced investigators throughout the Western world, covering such phenomena as mental healing, telepathy, remote viewing, out-of-body-experiences, psychokinesis, etc. These and allied phenomena are compatible with the findings of quantum physics, where the EPR paradox and Bell's theorem indicate that inert matter and consciousness are somehow inter-related. Yet biologists still maintain that living matter is not influenced by consciousness, and on the contrary, consciousness is an effect, not a cause, of life.

Instead of restricting ourselves to the extremes of *either* creation by Divine fiat *or* evolution by the adoption of random variations, a more credible answer might be found along the lines of directed evolution controlled by the activity of a non-physical agency operating on the plastic early stages of embryonic development, on the same broad principle as that demonstrated by tissue grafting experiments. A variation on this scene sees the body as a sort of sheath enclosing a nucleus of spirit surrounded by the soul or astral body. The spirit acquires its bodily sheath by a sort of condensation process, reminiscent of the formation of subatomic particles by condensation of energy into knots or vortices.

The foregoing abbreviated outline is intended only to give some idea of the broad scope of the Fix book, and cannot do justice to his breadth of vision, or the cogency of his arguments. I can only repeat my wholehearted recommendation of it; an admirable complement to this work.

Reverting now to the broad issues of the magnitude and origin of the universe, it may be difficult for those not already familiar with the subject to grasp all the implications. However, I think that any normally intelligent and open-minded person, with normal powers of critical appraisal, who took the trouble to ponder these implications thoughtfully, would find themselves bound to agree that the only credible explanation of it all is that it was the outcome of creative activity by a transcendental purposive intelligence. To conclude otherwise would be to deny the grandeur of harmony and order which we see in the vast universe around us, replacing it with total chaos. Surely only an imbecile or a doctrinaire crank could think like this. The obvious fact that we cannot explain the origin and existence of a transcendental intelligence does not in any way imply its non-existence, it merely demonstrates the limitations of the human mind.

As I wrote at the beginning of this chapter, it is not until one begins to get some feeling for the magnitude of the universe and its origin, that one begins to appreciate the sheer incongruity of any anthropomorphic concept of the creative source that brought it into existence. I presume that those who have followed me so far will begin to see what I meant. For my part, I find the 'God' suggested by a thoughtful study of the universe and the problems of its origin, far greater than the biblical figure of 'God the Father'. (Incidentally, why not 'God the Mother'?)

I don't know who originated the hackneyed phrase 'the mind boggles', but I find it entirely appropriate to my feelings when I try to imagine something of the awesome power that could not only bring a universe into existence, but maintain it in existence. If the near-infinite energy of the so-called vacuum were to be withdrawn even for a moment, the universe would vanish into nothingness. Einstein is reputed to have said, in a putative post-mortem communication, that energy can be seen as thought waves of the

Central Mind, the nucleus of *all* energy. This nucleus cannot be defined or analysed; the concentration of energy is so incredibly intense that it cannot be described even in scientific terms.[9] Scientists take all this for granted, quite content to talk about the constant production and annihilation of virtual particles from the zero-point energy of the vacuum, with never a thought as to how these particles acquire their unvarying characteristics of mass, charge, spin, etc.[70] They simply *assume* without thought, that it is in the nature of the vacuum energy to *form itself* into particles each having accurately controlled characteristics of mass, charge, spin. To my mind this assumption demonstrates an astonishing degree of naivety and wishful thinking on the part of scientists who claim to base their view and beliefs on reason rather than faith.

To sum up in the fewest words possible, I submit that the only truly rational explanation of the near-infinite energy which underlies and sustains the universe, is that it is an outflow or emanation from, an explication of, an advanced Implicate Order of transcendental mind or intelligence. And if such a transcendental power is necessary to account for the origin and continued existence of the universe of inert matter, then it becomes irrational to deny its intervention in the world of animate matter.

I am surprised at the fact that the Creationists, whether of fundamentalist or liberal persuasion, regard the Big Bang hypothesis as inimical to Biblical teaching, on the grounds that it controverts the principle that God created the world by fiat *ex nihilo*, out of nothing. It seems to me highly unlikely that the Bible writers had any conception of the energy which provides the underlying basis of matter, and on this assumption there is no conflict between the Big Bang hypothesis and the Bible. But if you take the word nothing or *nihilo* to mean absolute absence of both matter and energy, total nothingness, *then* there is conflict.

We have our being in a rational universe governed by immutable physical laws, and it seems reasonable to think that these laws originated in, were an expression of, the great transcendental intelligence which originated and sustains the universe. It seems reasonable too, to think that the creative activities of that intelligence will operate in accordance with the laws it originated. Once the laws are established, what would be the point of superseding them with lawless miracles? As I remarked above, it would be silly and presumptuous to think that we humans can ever understand the qualities and activities of the Source of all, but that is no reason why we should not use our gift of reason to appraise the most reasonable of the possible alternatives. To my mind, the scientific concept of creation commencing with pure energy, which is caused by pre-arranged physical laws to 'condense' into matter, is far more credible than the evangelical concept of miraculous creation out of nothingness by supernatural fiat.

An interesting book, *Intelligence Came First*, written by a group of well-qualified people is very relevant to these issues, and I can recommend it to all those who are interested in following this matter further.[84]

CHAPTER IX

MODES OF CREATION

Life fields. Perpetual motion. Implicate orders. The problem of evil solved.

It is time to return to the quandary raised by the seemingly irreconcilable findings that a) there are many things in nature which cannot be accounted for by Darwinian evolution, and b) the postulate of an omniscient, omnipotent beneficent Creator seems incompatible with the existence of so much waste and suffering in nature, with more than 990 out of every 1000 species failing to survive the hazards of existence.

I have already made the point that it would be illogical to argue that the transcendental intelligence necessary to account for the origin and sustained existence of the universe, might not also underlie the creation of life forms. But it seems to me somewhat presumptive to assume that this awesome intelligence should be directly responsible for the near-infinity of details associated with the great multiplicity of life forms in the universe. We are so used to thinking in terms of terrestrial life that we overlook the probability of innumerable other life forms in the universe. If only one star in a million had a planet suitable for life, and if only one in a million of *these* was actually a home for life, this would still mean something like *100 billion* inhabited planets, many of which might well have species far more highly developed than Homo sapiens. To assume that a single intelligence handled all the details of this infinite variety of complex life would be something like assuming that the managing director of a great multi-national corporation personally handled every detail of the daily activity of his far-flung empire. I am not trying to suggest an analogy between the ultimate Source and a human leader, but I see no reason why we should not use our little human intellect and imagination to seek the most reasonable of the various possibilities we can find.

During the last seven decades, the physicists' concept of immaterial fields as the basic reality underlying the physical world has been echoed by thinkers in the life sciences. In the early 1920s morphogenetic (form controlling) fields were proposed by Spemann, Gurwitsch, Weiss, followed later by Smuts, Weissman, and others, two of the most recent being Sheldrake[81] and Evans.[26] As Sheldrake explains, the popular impression that the magical double-helix molecule of DNA and its derivatives can account for all the phenomena of embryology and morphology is conjecture rather than knowledge. Prof. Brian Goodwin of The Open University asserts firmly that DNA does *not* code for development of the embryo, it only contains instructions for building molecules, and we have no real knowledge of how molecules are built into organisms.[29]

Experimental evidence for the existence of electrical and electro-magnetic fields associated with biological organisms has been obtained by a number of workers, including Burr and Northrop, Lakhovsky, Tiller, Milner, Smart, Jaffe and Evans. The instrument used by Burr is a high-impedance voltmeter drawing negligible current, and it was unnecessary to make contact with the skin to obtain readings. The voltage gradients in a frog's egg show the future location of the nervous system before it has started to form.[79] Interestingly, an independent confirmation of this has been given by Talbot, who found that the longitudinal axis of a salamander's tail remains unaltered when early cells in the embryo are experimentally re-positioned; the cells adjust to their new position without altering the axis.[88]

Jaffe and his co-workers at Purdue University, Indiana, used a vibrating electrode generating a controlled-frequency A.C. signal with excellent discrimination against random noise signals.[67] He found the outward growth of the migratory tips of nerve cells and muscle cells was strongly influenced by small applied fields. And the regeneration of limbs in salamanders and frogs was accompanied by local fields, and could be strongly influenced by applying external fields. It has been found independently that sliced-off finger tips will regenerate if left open, not sutured, and that this is also accompanied by autonomic local fields similar to those found in salamander regeneration.

John Evans' book presents an intriguing picture of the morphological effects of biomagnetic fields, based on body measurements with high-sensitivity super-conducting magnetometers using quantum interference principles.[26] He provides a number of fascinating computer-graphics simulations of biomagnetic waveforms based on cerebrospinal electromagnetic resonances, which afford an exciting glimpse of the possible scope of such fields in embryology and morphology. The book may not be easy reading for the layman due to its technical content, but it should encourage an open minded reconsideration of some of the over-rigid conventions of orthodox materialistic science.

Another scientist, Dr Evan Harris Walker, has developed a theory of the interaction of consciousness and brain, based on quantum-mechanical processes at synaptic clefts in the neural networks.[93] This is highly technical, but can be roughly summarised by saying that he equates consciousness with the non-physical 'hidden variables' postulated by some scientists as the factor which decides the actual outcome of an unpredictable Uncertainty event. One of Walker's speculations is that the universe may be 'inhabited' by an unlimited number of elementary units of consciousness responsible for its detailed working.

More recently, the distinguished brain scientist Sir John Eccles has proposed a like system of brain-mind interaction based on quantum-mechanical effects at synaptic clefts.[21] He writes in terms of mental fields analogous to the 'probability fields' of quantum physics, which carry neither mass nor energy but can interact with physical systems through autonomous energy-exchange effects, and are thus able to affect the vesicular activity at microsites in the synaptic junctions in the cerebral cortex.

The biologist Lyall Watson gives some instances of extraordinary animal behaviour which seems impossible to account for as the outcome of random variations, and concludes that something over and above the genetic system must be involved.[94] He postulates a 'contingent system', a sort of supervening influence which is always there, dreaming its dreams and biding its time until a vehicle suited to its manifestation appears on the scene. It provides an information flux connecting allied species and behaviour, and is able to make use of the potential variation content of the excess DNA present in all organisms. Its expression is psychical rather than physical, and this has clear parallels with the life-field hypotheses already mentioned.

Thus the hypothesis of morphogenetic fields, or life fields for short, has been endorsed by contemporary scientists, and seems to be well supported by experimental evidence. There seems no reason why these life fields should not be the answer to the problem of how the molecules built by the DNA code are assembled into organisms. Nor can I see any good reason why they should not be seen as the means adopted by the ultimate Source to control the infinitude of details involved in the building of organisms. This does not imply that the organising fields are directly controlled by the Source. They could conceivably have some degree of individual autonomy. This thought leads to a system of philosophy originated by the philosopher Douglas Fawcett, brother of the explorer Col Percy Fawcett.

I refer to his little-known philosophy of Imaginism, based essentially on the postulate that the primary function of creative mind or spirit is not reason or thought, but imagination.[27] Imagination originates, then reason takes over and analyses, assesses, proves or rejects. God or the ultimate Source is pure imagining – the Divine Imaginal, to use Fawcett's term. What It imagines, comes into being: *is* reality. Divine imagining has two complementary and inseparable aspects, additive which creates novelty, and conservative which sustains in existence that which is created by the additive aspect.

This may be a difficult concept for those conditioned by a lifetime of orthodox thinking, but when one stops to analyse it, it makes sense. Reason can easily be seen as deriving from imagination, whereas the converse seems less likely. Qualities such as amusement, beauty, colour, hope, love, sorrow, seem more likely to derive from imagination than from reason. And it is easy to see invention as a matter of imagination, backed by reason which analyses and assesses. Of course our little human spark of imagination is infinitely far removed from divine imagining. We can focus our attention, like a quickly fading phosphorescent spot, on one thing at a time, but the Divine Imaginal can focus on all things simultaneously in an all-inclusive continuum of past, present and future.[46] One can visualise a progressive scale of the 'specious present', the duration of the *now*, going up from the human span of perhaps a fraction of a second, all the way to infinity for the ultimate Source.

In passing, it is interesting to consider the thought that the conservative aspect of the Divine Imaginal may be displayed in the perpetual motion of the elementary particles inside the atoms which are the basis of physical matter. Perpetual motion is a scientific impossibility in any man-made product, but *some* source of energy sustains the atoms of matter in perpetual motion.

And this sustaining conserving aspect is also reflected in a small way in our selves, in the form of memory, which sustains in existence our personal background of experience and knowledge. The additive aspect is reflected in our creative urge and the satisfaction gained from the successful completion of a creative task, whether it be writing a book, making a tool, building a garden, or whatever.

The ultimate Source is seen by Fawcett not as an extrinsic being or person, but an 'all-pervasive immaterial field of creative spirituality outside time and space', to borrow a phrase of Sir Kelvin Spencer's.[92] This Divine Imaginal or Source is not one God directly creating everything personally, but the fountainhead of a vast cosmic hierarchy of primary and secondary imaginals going all the way down the scale from galactic to subatomic. Each of the galaxies, separated by inconceivable depths of space, may be under the control of a Primary Imaginal, a finite 'God' wise and powerful beyond human comprehension, but not infinitely so. Raynor Johnson made the interesting point that the immense spaces between galaxies, running into millions of light-years, may permit different types of imaginal experiments to proceed without mutual interference.[46]

At each stage of inorganic or organic evolution, waiting sub-imaginals are able to descend into matter and manifest their characteristics. For instance, the combination of one atom of oxygen and two atoms of hydrogen provides appropriate conditions for the water imaginal to manifest, and so on for the myriads of atomic and molecular combinations possible. This may sound fanciful to the chemist, but it could explain the unique properties of water, which are essential to all life as we know it. It could also explain the mystery of snow crystals, all of which have a basically six-sided or six-armed symmetrical form, yet no two are identical when studied under the microscope. The crystal grows outwards from a nucleus such as a dust speck or spore, and the question arises of how each of the six sides or arms exactly replicates its neighbours while differing from its teeming myriads of fellow crystals. This is quite a remarkable phenomenon, inexplicable by material causes, but simply accounted for by Imaginism.

Another example is colour, which we have seen to be inexplicable in purely material terms (pages 50–54). The mysterious unknown link between colour and wavelength can easily be accounted for by Imaginism, but not by materialism. And we find strong support for the idea that imagination, not reason, is the primary activity of creative spirit – it is much easier to regard colour as springing from imagination than from reason.

Imaginism explains the emergence of new properties from new combinations of parts. Each manifestation of new properties is accounted for by higher imaginals descending into the products of lower imaginals, in a continuous hierarchy extending all the way from quark to man. Our little spark of human imagining is able to 'resonate' with the creative imagining and thus perceive the created qualities. This is reminiscent of Rupert Sheldrake's concept of mutually resonating morphogenetic fields.[81] Qualities like colour, scent, sound, are not, as some have argued, mere products of our minds, they have an independent reality as products of the imaginal concerned.

I find it instructive to compare this thinking with that of the 18th century philsopher George Berkeley, who held that nothing can exist in the absence of mind; if it is not perceived by a created mind, it must subsist in a Creative Mind if it is to have any existence at all. IIc maintained that sensory perceptions are impressed on the human mind, not by the physical world, but by the mind of God, where everything originates and is held in existence. Like acting on like seems more reasonable than unlike acting on unlike. If you equate Berkeley's word 'God' with Fawcett's concept of a hierarchical organisation of creative imaginals, you have a striking similarity of thought.

It has become fashionable to regard Berkeleyan philosophy with disfavour, as an extreme form of Idealism, but those who do so, seem not to realise that it is entirely in keeping with the views of an eminent contemporary physicist, Prof. David Bohm. In his famous hypothesis of the Implicate Order discussed in Chapter VIII, Bohm postulates an undifferentiated Primary Reality of pure vibration or energy, capable of an infinite variety of physical expressions.[7,8] It is caused to take the form of the separate objects displayed by sensory perceptions, by the act of conscious attention. It is not difficult to see the parallels between Bohm's Implicate Order, Berkeley's mind of God, and Fawcett's Divine Imaginal. Nor is it difficult to see the similarity of principle between these and the life fields of Burr, Jaffe, Sheldrake, Evans et al., the consciousness units of E. H. Walker, and the contingent system of Lyall Watson.

The broad picture presented by Imaginism is essentially hierarchical (Figure 8). There is a hierarchy of freedom, creativity, and consciousness, descending from a maximum at the top of the spiritual level down through ever-decreasing levels to a minimum at the bottom of the physical level, and there is a corresponding hierarchy of reality, again in descending levels down to the mineral. (Note the concordance with Bohm.[8]) The Primary imaginals created by the Fountainhead, the Divine Imaginal to use Fawcett's term,

105

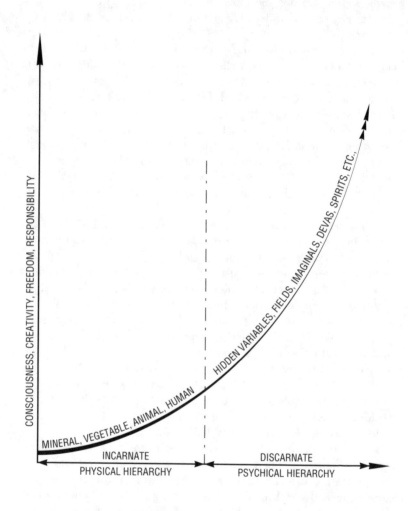

Figure 8

evolved by creating secondary imaginals, and these in turn evolved by creating sub-imaginals right down to the subatomic level. Each successive stage had a lesser degree of freedom and responsibility, and each was a pale reflection of the higher stage from which it was descended. The psychic hierarchy, evolved in descending order, was brought into interaction with a physical hierarchy evolved in ascending order, from mineral to vegetable and animal, and finally man. With the biological advent of man, the stage was set for the manifestation of some degree of self-awareness and free-will in the physical world, together with other spiritual qualities such as beauty, humour, joy. It was in this way that the ultimate Source chose to create portions of itself capable of bringing into existence all the world's masterpieces which had previously no existence other than as its own 'dreams'. This was the way It attained self-expression.

In achieving all this, the possibility of error and evil came into existence. Creativity could not be given without some degree of free-will – an automaton could not create genuine novelty and innovation. But with the gift of free-will, the power to choose, to originate, man was given the power to choose evil as well as good, to be self-seeking, to dominate and repress, maltreat and abuse. Disharmony and rebellion, envy and greed, conflict and strife, arose. And in addition to this inevitable outcome of man's autonomy, there was always the possibility of error arising from imperfections or inadequacies in the lower ranks of the imaginal hierarchy. Only the ultimate Source, the fountainhead, the Divine Imaginal, is all-wise and all-powerful; the lesser imaginals going down through the hierarchy, although wise and powerful beyond our little human understanding, are something less than perfect. They may sometimes make errors of judgement or indulge in experiments just for the thrill of it. As suggested on page 63, the sheer joy of creation may lead to an excess of activity going far beyond the minimum requirement of maintaining balance in the biosphere. The problem of reconciling the emergence of vast numbers of new species over and above the capacity of the biosphere, leading to mass extinctions on a similarly vast scale, becomes less intransigent if the concept of personal creation by an omniscient omnipotent Divinity is replaced by the concept of delegated creation by a vast hierarchy of subordinate but largely-autonomous powers.

It would, of course, be absurd to think that we humans can ever understand, let alone describe, the nature, origin, and activities of the infinite Source, and the most we can attempt is a reasoned guess at logical possibilities. For my part, I find this in the philosophy of Imaginism. I have been able here to provide only a very brief inadequate outline of Fawcett's philosophy, but I hope it will suffice to illustrate its powers of explanation.

The only internal problem I can see in this philosophy is that of defining what is meant by the word 'imaginal', but that is a side issue, not an objection of principle. I can see no *a priori* objections of principle. Darwinists are likely to raise the objection that it is merely an untestable version of mysticism, using the word pejoratively, but there is no substance in this objection, since Darwinism itself is also untestable. Kitcher has admitted as much, although he seeks to counter the admission by arguing that Darwinism is no more untestable than the rest of science, a counter which as we have seen (page 66) doesn't hold water.[48]

It matters little whether imaginals are equated with life fields or a contingent system, or are regarded as spiritual entities which can influence physical matter directly. The important thing is the principle that there is a non-physical realm of creative spirituality which originated and sustains the universe, and continues to influence, perhaps with the aid of a vast cosmic hierarchy of subordinate creative powers, the infinite variety of natural phenomena.

Not only is Imaginism free from logical objections of principle, but it is positively supported by a number of practical points. It eliminates the much debated problem of evil in a world created by an omnipotent God. It removes the logical implausibility, not to say incongruity, of personal creation by a single almighty Deity, of the near-infinite variety of natural phenomena and life forms, accompanied by much waste and inefficiency on an obvious trial-and-error basis. I find it entirely congruent with the views of many thinkers such as Berkeley, Bohm, Evans, Goodwin, Sheldrake, Walker, Lyall Watson, and others mentioned above. And it is a

108

complete rational answer to the quandary mentioned above (page 77) without destroying the basic principle of either religion or progressive evolution, using the word in the broad sense.

In respect of religion, Imaginism retains the underlying principle of creation by a transcendent spiritual power, and requires only that it be aided by a hierarchical organisation of subordinate powers. This is not essentially different to the already-accepted concept of a hierarchy of angels and archangels, so I do not see any reason for theologians to object.

And in respect of Evolution, it retains the basic principle of gradual progressive evolution by the selection of advantageous variations, and requires only an acceptance of the point that genetic mutations are not necessarily caused *only* by physical influences, and may sometimes be caused by non-physical influences which by definition are unknown to physical science. Since it cannot be proved that only physical factors can act on genes, I cannot see any logical reason to reject the possibility of purposive direction. Nor does it make sense to deny the whole concept of a non-physical realm, in view of the undeniable reality of non-physical qualities such as amusement, aspiration, awe, consciousness, imagination, joy, love, pity, pride, reason, volition, and so on.

But although the existence of a non-physical realm cannot be refuted in principle, the materialist could still reject it as a practical influence in biology, on the basis that we cannot say exactly how it intervenes in physical activities. I can see no substance in this argument. The fact that we cannot say how something operates is no argument against its existence. We don't know how volition causes muscular activity, but this does not mean that it can't happen. If Prof. Goodwin is correct in saying that genes are not the direct sole cause of embryonic development[29] – and I am sure he is – then genetic mutations cannot be the sole cause of structural variations in biological organisms, and the postulate of life fields acting directly on the embryo becomes a logical one. As I see it, it doesn't really matter very much what they are called – life fields, morphogenetic fields, biomagnetic fields, energy fields, or just fields of influence – it's the principle that matters, rather than the precise nomenclature.

CHAPTER X

SUMMING UP AND REVIEW

Principles at issue. Mutiny in the ranks. Fact versus fiction. Darwin's theology. Psychological factors. The great brain explosion.

Having covered a wide range of problems in the proverbial nutshell, it may be opportune to summarise briefly our main conclusions.

1)   The only intelligible explanation of the origin and continued existence of the universe (involving the empty void, the universal energy, the Big Bang, the subatomic particles with controlled characteristics of mass, charge, spin, and all the associated critical constants) is that it was and is the result of purposive intervention by a transcendental source, a creative intelligence immeasurably superior to the totality of human intelligence.

2)   It is impossible to account satisfactorily for some of the phenomena of nature (such as colour, snow crystals, metamorphosis of insects, sensory organs, etc.) in terms of Darwinian or Neo-Darwinian evolution by the natural selection of random variations; and there are no *a priori* logical grounds for denying the intervention in nature of a transcendental creative power or powers. The potential objection that this hypothesis is untestable carries no weight, since the alternative hypothesis of chance is equally untestable.

3)   The amount of experimental trial-and-error in nature, with its inevitable wastage and suffering, makes it seem inappropriate to

equate the creative power or powers of (2) with the supreme Source of (1) above. This difficulty is avoided by postulating a largely-autonomous hierarchy of creative sub-powers or fields of influence, variously described by philosophers as Implicate Orders, imaginals, hidden variables, morphogenetic fields, biomagnetic fields, energy fields, life fields, contingent systems, etc.

4) Genes carry instructions for building molecules, not organisms. The fields of (3) could be the means by which molecules are built into organisms.

Between them, these four points can account for the following phenomena of nature better than can Darwinian evolutionary theory:

a) The existence of the universe and its primal energy.
b) Perpetual motion of the subatomic particles.
c) The emergence of life in the world of inert matter.
d) The imperative will to live and reproduce, which characterises all life.
e) The existence of a fully-operative reproductive system in radically new life forms.
f) The sequential growth of functionally-related parts in a biological organism.
g) The emergence in established biological organisms of advantageous new structures which offer no advantage until functionally complete.
h) Periodic outbursts of speciation activity making good the losses due to extinction.
i) The existence of non-physical qualities such as beauty, colour, consciousness, humour, imagination, music, reason, scent, volition, etc.,

to mention only a few of the more basic examples.

Little of this is entirely new. According to Holdroyd,[39] Darwin's friend and *confidante* Asa Gray was one of the first to propound the idea that mutations might be controlled by God as a means of directing evolution, although this idea was rejected at the time, on the grounds that God would not be likely to resort to such an inefficient means of control.[39] But is it inefficient? The genetic system provides a very accurate and reliable means of maintaining the integrity of species despite the unavoidable incidence of occasional copying mishaps; and it seems to me that controlled modifications to the genes could be an efficient practical way of introducing advantageous modifications of structure without pre-judicing this integrity. And there is also the possibility of controlled modifications of the life fields postulated as directing the sequential development of the embryo. If Fawcett's philosophy of Imaginism had been known in Darwin's day, I suspect that Asa Gray's suggestion might have received a more constructive response.

Brian Leith has made the point that since publication of *The Origin of Species*, Darwinian principles have seeped into every corner of our worldview, and 'the philosophy implied by Darwinism is that life may have no purpose in the traditional sense, and is ultimately a random process'.[51] But, he claims, in the past decade a new breed of biologists has emerged who are considered scientifically respectable, but have doubts about Darwinism. Other writers have said the same thing. Some of those who are reputed to have expressed doubts of one sort or another are—

D. Axelford	P. P. Grassé	N. Platnick
von Bertalanffy	von Haeme	D. Raup
H. Beurlen	B. Halstead	A. Romer
Hampton Carson	G. A. Kerkut	Steven Stanley
Ernst Chain	Mootoo Kimura	Ted Steele
Bryan Clarke	D. B. Kitts	Gunther Stent
E. Conklin	J. P. Lehman	Karl Stern
E. S. Deevy	Richard Levins	E. Swinton
T. Dobzhansky	R. Lewontin	Howard Temin
G. A. Dover	L. Matthews	Tome
Murray Eden	Norman Mcbeth	C. H. Waddington
Lorne Eisley	C. Nelson	Rupert Weidl
Peter Forey	Yomoko Ohta	Paul Weiss
T. H. Frazzeta	E. C. Olsen	H. Wehrli
Duane Gish	Oparin.	E. White
R. B. Goldschmidt	H. F. Osborn	C. P. Williams
Brian Goodwin	Colin Patterson	

Note   The foregoing names have been taken from References 35, 51, 75, 89. It is probable that further names would be found in a more extensive search, perhaps running into three figures in all. Apologies to anyone who feels wrongly included or excluded!

With so many dissenters in the ranks of the biologists and palaeontologists, it seems a little surprising that evolutionary theory is still taught as established fact in our classrooms and lecture halls. Most text books either ignore, or at best provide totally inadequate explanations of, the sort of problem outlined in the preceding pages. For instance, Maynard Smith, one of our foremost evolutionists, explains the evolution of structures having interacting parts which all have to be present before they can function properly and confer survival advantage, by postulating that 'a new structure evolves at first because it confers advantage by performing one function, but in time it can effectively perform a different function'.[85] He then instances membranes of pterodactyls and bats used for gliding before flying; some arboreal animals with body membranes which allegedly conferred advantage by disguising their shadows from predators; and the lungs of lungfish which enabled them to live in shallow water before their descendants walked on dry land. He goes on 'These examples show that there is no reason to suppose that even the most complex structures underwent a long period of evolution and elaboration before they could function and so confer selection advantage'. Do they indeed! I should have thought that the evolution of feathered wings was a major job requiring many intermediate steps after the evolution of membranes. And what different function could an incipient eye fulfil? It seems fair to suggest that this sweeping conclusion is inadequately based.

Kitcher endorses the same point, but (perhaps wisely!) *without* the aid of examples.[48] He asserts blandly, 'The most common explanation of evolutionary novelties appeals to change of function'. An organ develops because it provides a certain advantage, and once developed 'beyond a certain point' it can be put to unanticipated uses. Facile seems the right word.

Mark Ridley's explanation of the evolution of the eye can be described as starry-eyed rather than down-to-earth.[74] A coating of light-sensitive pigment arises from a single mutation and positions itself at the bottom of a bowl-shaped depression in the epidermis – no need for connection to a nerve system apparently. Then the bowl enlarges itself, and a pin-hole aperture forms itself, after which gymnastics the space between pigment and pin-hole becomes filled with jelly allegedly acting as a lens and permitting enlargement of the pin-hole. The next simple step is for the jelly to be replaced by a true optical lens. A few further minor refinements such as a focusing mechanism are added, and lo and behold, we finish up with a complex co-adapted organ 'without the need for an impossible coincidence of random mutations'.

Ralph Estling cites some experiments which demonstrate (*with the aid of models!*) that incipient insect wings or winglets, although too short to be of use for flight, conferred advantage by acting as solar heat collectors.[68] Presumably when the winglets grew longer, the insects decided they no longer needed their heat collectors, and instead of discarding them, simply grew flight muscles to flap them up and down.

Richard Dawkins seems not to grasp that a problem exists, being quite content to present his sufficient-number-of-finely-graded-intermediate-steps hypothesis as a universal cure-all for any difficulty.[19]

Apart from these examples of inadequate explanations of specific problems, evolutionists delight in making use of assumptions to prove their validity. Here are some typical examples of unjustifiable assumptions asserted as if they were fact:

Jacques Monod: Pure Chance, absolutely free but blind, at the very root of the stupendous edifice of evolution . . . is today the sole conceivable hypothesis . . .[57]

Julian Huxley: The first point to make about Darwin's theory is that it is no longer a theory, but a fact.[35]

Ashley Montagu: Evolution is a fact, not a theory. It was once a theory, but today . . . it is probably the best authenticated actuality known to science.[59]

G. G. Simpson: Darwin was one of history's towering geniuses and ranks with the greatest heroes of man's intellectual progress. He deserves this place because he finally and definitely established evolution as fact, no longer speculation or an alternative hypothesis.[83]
R. A. Fisher: The most apparently improbable adaptations, provided they confer a biological advantage, are so many demonstrations of the immense power of natural selection over the stretches of geological time.[43]

This brief examination of a few examples of the propensity of authors of evolutionary books to present opinion and conjecture as established fact, is an eye-opener. I think it fair comment to say that in no other branch of science are there practitioners to be found who are so easily satisfied with such complacent slap-dash expositions of their speciality. There must be a reason for this unusual state of affairs. Montagu has described the attributes of a scientist thus: 'A scientist is characterised neither by a willingness to believe or a willingness to disbelieve, nor yet by a desire to prove or disprove anything, but by the desire to establish what *is*, and to do so by observation, experiment, verification, and falsification'.[59] By this definition it seems that evolutionists are not really scientists! It seems clear that they are keen to establish evolution as established fact, and loth to give serious consideration to anyone who presents a case for thinking otherwise. And just look again at G. G. Simpson's eulogy of Darwin above – is there any justification for this resounding acclaim? What did Darwin himself have to say about his motives and thinking? He wrote 'There seems to me too much misery in the world. I cannot persuade myself that a beneficent and omnipotent God would have created the ichneumonidae with the express intention of their feeding on the bodies of living caterpillars, or that a cat should play with a [living] mouse'.[17]
A lot of us feel like this, and can think of more weighty examples too, but if Darwin had been the heroic intellectual figure that Simpson blandly asserts, then I suggest that it might have occurred to him that creation did not *necessarily* imply a divine omnipotent

Creator as the only possible source of creation. On another occasion Darwin wrote 'My theology is in a simple muddle; I cannot look at the universe as the result of blind chance, yet I cannot see any evidence . . . of design in the details. On the other hand, I cannot anyhow be contented to view this wonderful universe, and conclude that everything is the result of brute force. I am inclined to look at everything as resulting from designed laws, with the details . . . left to the workings of what we may call chance. Not that this *at all* satisfies me'. (His italics.)

It is quite clear, surely, that Darwin's theory was conjecture based on nothing more weighty than his personal inability to reconcile the sufferings in the world of nature with his interpretation of religious doctrine and dogma. Darwin's genius seems to have resided in his ability to collect and marshall into a coherent whole, a large body of isolated observations, rather than in a capacity for deep analytical thought. Contrary to what Simpson asserts so unequivocally, it was not Darwin who 'finally and definitely established evolution as a fact', it was his followers, who by constant repetition persuaded themselves that it was fact.

This circumstance seems to me to provide an explanation of the whole situation. In the last paragraph of Darwin's famous *Origin* we find the words 'There is grandeur in this view of life, with its several powers, having been breathed by the Creator into a few forms or into one'. Hardly the words of a man intending to spread a world-wide belief that ultimately life is a purposeless random process. As Montagu points out, Darwin described himself not as an atheist, but an agnostic. Unlike Darwin, his followers discarded altogether the concept of a Creative Source underlying the workings of nature, and have made great efforts to account for the origin of life in purely physical terms, as we noted in Chapter VIII. I have already pointed out one basic difficulty in explaining how life could arise from non-life, namely the problem of how the imperative instinct of self-preservation and reproduction which characterises *all* life, could arise from any particular form or forms of life.

Whilst Darwin seems to have taken it for granted that the variations acted upon by natural selection were undirected and purely random relative to the organism's needs, he never, as far as I know, asserted categorically that this was necessarily always the case; and I suspect that if challenged on the point he would have conceded that there was no actual evidence for it, and no *a priori* reason making it inevitable. Yet his followers invariably regard it as undeniable proven fact, or at least give that impression.

One more point on which Darwin's own views merit consideration is the problem of complex organs with interacting parts which must all be present if it is to function properly and confer advantage. Darwin openly admitted there was indeed a problem, saying it seemed 'absurd in the highest possible degree' to suppose that the eye, with all its inimitable contrivances for focusing over a wide range of distances, for varying the iris aperture, for correcting spherical and chromatic aberrations, and so on, could have been formed by natural selection acting on fortuitous variations. But he maintained that if 'large bodies of facts' *can* be explained by natural selection, we have no reason to stop short at the eye and like complex organs. He suggested that in considering evolution of the eye, we ought to imagine a layer of transparent tissue overlying a light-sensitive nerve, and to suppose every part of this layer slowly changing in density so as to separate into different layers placed at different distances from each other, and with the surface of each layer slowly changing form . . . over periods of 'millions on millions of years'. I must confess I find this a little difficult to follow, but presume Darwin was trying to imagine ways in which a lens and retina might have formed. But he over-looked the obvious problem of how the useless intermediate stages of the process could have been selected for survival advantage. As an answer to the self-admitted charge of absurdity in the highest possible degree, it fails to convince.

I find it curious that, despite Darwin's awareness of the fact that mankind had for centuries been selectively breeding plants and animals with the conscious intention of producing improved varieties thereof, he should nevertheless propound a theory of evolution which denied the intervention of consciousness in nature. And the same thing applies also to evolutionists who, with conscious

117

intent, seek to demonstrate the spontaneous self-activated generation of life in purely physical terms devoid of any conscious control. Why should a creature whose activities are decided by conscious intent deny the intervention of conscious intent in the activities of the world of nature?

Many evolutionists will, I suspect, react angrily to my statement that Darwin did *not* establish evolution as a fact, taking it as slur on his genius. Nevertheless, his background thinking set out above, supports my view. It is quite clear that he found himself unable to reconcile the amount of suffering in the world of nature with the religious doctrine of a benign, omnipotent Creator, and sought an answer to this difficulty. He thought he could see one in the theory of evolution, with the long-continued accumulation of advantageous small variations selected by survival advantage, eventually adding up to a large total which represented a new species unable to interbreed with the original form. He carried this conjecture to the point of assuming that, in principle, it might be capable of explaining the whole range of existing species in terms of descent from one or a few original forms. He realised that evidence in support of this conjecture could only be found in the fossil record, but was disappointed to find that the record was too incomplete to be of much use, and pinned his hopes on the probability of future finds being unearthed to support his conjectures. These hopes were to be partially fulfilled, but only partially, as we have seen.

One of the reasons why Darwin's theory caught on so quickly and achieved scientific respectability, was that it provided a welcome escape route for those who, in increasing number, were suspicious of religious doctrine, and resentful of the discouragement of freedom of thought by the Churches. An associated factor was the immense success science was achieving with the reductionist, mechanistic, materialistic approach. This success went to their heads, and made them loth to run any risk of taking the easy way out of a difficult problem by simply giving up and saying 'Well, God must have made it that way'. Scientists jumped on the Darwinian bandwagon enthusiastically, and lost no time in telling each other what a genius the man was, with the result that they came, almost unconsciously, to believe it. It is well known to advertisers that if you keep telling people that X is a wonderful product, many of them come to believe you, irrespective of the real merits of X.

A further factor in the affair has emerged since the *Origin* was published, one that I touched on in the Preface. As explosive expansion of knowledge has taken place in the life sciences, and biologists have become so deeply immersed in assimilating, amplifying, refining and deploying all this new knowledge that they have found little time or inclination to think about the basic problems of principle inhering in evolutionary theory – problems of the sort I have outlined in the preceding pages. Since Darwin's day, a vast intellectual structure of evolutionary theory, mostly favourable to the concept, has been built up – evolved! – and evolutionists have been so deeply immersed in this great intellectual edifice that they have lost sight of the more homespun realm of elementary first principles, and can think only in terms of the great wealth of professional hypotheses favourable to evolutionary theory. They tend to assume that the fundamental problems have already been answered – as to some small extent they have – and to dismiss them as 'old hat', to quote Dawkins once again.[92]

In 1869 A. R. Wallace, co-founder of evolution by natural selection, wrote to Darwin, pointing out that natural selection could only provide the savage with a brain a little superior to that of an ape, whereas he was in fact endowed with one only slightly inferior to that of the average member of our learned Societies.[22] Darwin could only make the lame reply that he hoped Wallace had not too completely murdered their child. What Wallace meant was that natural selection could not act to select a biological structure in advance of its needs, or before it could use it to advantage, and no doubt Darwin could see this and answered in about the only way open to him. Ironically, Darwin was led to observe in later life that if, as he fully believed, the mind of man evolved from a more elementary mind such as that of the lowest animal, then a doubt must arise as to how far his mind could be trusted in drawing so far-reaching a conclusion. In other words, he, Darwin, could have been wrong after all.[17]

There are three separate problems arising from Wallace's

119

observation, firstly the one he directly referred to, namely how natural selection could act on a feature before its time; secondly the problem of how consciousness could arise from variations in a physical structure; and thirdly the problem of how so extraordinarily rapid an expansion could arise from random variations anyway. The last of these, the problem of a big change in a short time, was not fully understood at that date, and merits some consideration.

In the last million years (a fleeting moment in evolutionary time) the brain has almost doubled in size, from about 800 gms to 1400 gms.[22] This enormous increase of some 600 gms (1¼ lbs) took place mainly in the neocortex, with its ten billion neurones (nerve cells) interconnected by about ten trillion synaptic junctions, plus the 300 million commisural fibres of the *corpus callosum* linking the two cerebral hemispheres, and the millions of myelinated fibres connecting the cortex to other parts of the brain such as the thalamus, hippocampus, cerebellum, limbic system, etc.

All this means that something like 5,000 million neurones, *each* with thousands of interconnected synaptic junctions, plus say a million commisural fibres and further millions of myelinated fibres going to other parts of the brain, must have been added during that million-year period. In other words, an average of fourteen neurones, each with thousands of associated synapses and commisural fibres, were added *every day* throughout that million-year period. And not just added piecemeal, but built into a highly organised complex of functional zones (the lobes and Brodman areas) comprising millions of module units each containing thousands of neurones of various types (pyramidal, stellate, excitatory, inhibitory, etc.), and each with their complement of axon, dendrites, synapses, and afferent fibres.[22]

This fantastic enlargement of the brain was completed about 100,000 years ago, long before its potential could be utilised, as Wallace pointed out to Darwin. If as much had been known then about the complexity of the brain as is known now, I suspect that Darwin would have been forced to conclude that their mutual child had been well and truly laid to rest!

The quite extraordinary speed at which this expansion of the brain occurred is matched only by the extraordinary nature of the mind which now uses that magnificent brain. Able to probe the innermost workings of the atom and of the vast universe with giant particle-accelerator machines and theories of quantum mechanics, and to uncover the structure of the famous double-helix molecule of DNA; yet seemingly powerless to free himself from the shackles of long-crystallised dogma. Standing back and looking with a fresh eye at the miraculous (I use the word deliberately) growth of the brain outlined above, it seems to me abundantly clear that it could not by any legitimate stretch of the imagination be seen as the outcome of fortuitous genetic mutations. It is relevant to add that in a recent new book, *The Mirror of Creation*,[99] by a highly respected scientist in the field of cell biology, the information content involved in the formation of the interconnected neural circuitry of the cerebral cortex is estimated to be in the region of $10^{30,000,000,000,000}$, an unimaginably vast figure which rules out any possibility of random formation.

Richard Dawkins bravely quotes a well-known passage from Darwin's *Origin*: 'If it could be demonstrated that any complex organ existed which could not possibly have been formed by numerous successive slight modifications, my theory would absolutely break down'. Dawkins comments 'I do not believe that such a case will ever be found. If it is – it will have to be *really* complex . . . I shall cease to believe in Darwinism'.[19/91] Well, if Darwin had known as much about the brain as we now know, I think he would have had to accept that his theory really had broken down! So how about it, Dr Dawkins? Is the *brain* complex enough for you?

Dawkins admits 'Serious argument and criticism is a vitally important part of any science [and] there have been times in the history of science when the whole of orthodox science has been rightly thrown over because of a single awkward fact. It would be arrogant to assume that such overthrows will never happen again'.[19/251,293] Kitcher also admits '. . . history is a powerful reminder that the mightiest theories may fall'.[48] G. R. Taylor observed with restraint 'The probability that there are forces at work in the universe of which we have as yet no inkling, is not too bizarre to entertain'.[89]

121

And Eccles stresses the great importance of a critical examination of established theories from time to time, particularly when they tend to harden into dogma.[22] Although himself a staunch Darwinian, he admits freely that evolutionary theory fails in *at least* one crucial respect – it cannot account for the existence of thinking self-conscious beings like ourselves. He cites Schopenhaur: 'Materialism is the philosophy of the subject who has forgotten to take account of himself', and observes 'the profound tragedy of our age is that the religious vision [of for instance Sherrington and Schrödinger] has become dimmed or rejected'.

The reasoned amalgam of Creationism and Evolutionism here proposed, is clearly in concordance with these various views. It retains the *principle* of progressive evolution by the natural selection of advantageous variations, subject only to acceptance of the *possibility* of transcendental direction of variations. It leaves open the possibility of random unguided mutations, and leaves assessment of the likely proportion of directed to random, to individual judgement. Personally, I think it likely that the great majority are directed, and only a small minority random or undirected, but others may judge differently.

And it retains the *principle* of creation, subject only to acceptance of the *possibility* of creation being delegated to a hierarchy of transcendental powers. It leaves open the possibility of creative activity by a single Divinity, and leaves assessment of the likely proportion of divine to delegated, to individual judgement. Personally, I think it likely that the great majority are delegated, and only a small minority directly handled by the Divinity, but others may again judge differently.

If Charles Darwin could have foreseen that a century after his death, it was going to be said that Darwinian principles had seeped into every corner of our worldview, carrying with them the implication that life has no purpose, and is ultimately a purposeless random process, he would, I think, have been deeply shocked. This outcome was clearly not his intention, and it would be unfair to put the blame on his shoulders. Rather it must rest mainly on those of his disciples who immediately embraced it with little real thought, and lost no time in building it into a great edifice of conjecture and speculation masquerading as established fact.

We all tend to fall in love with our own ideas, and often experience real difficulty in forming a reliable judgement of their worth. Charles Darwin was an honest and fair-minded man, meticulous in his work, and he attempted to take into account some at least of the criticisms which his great work the *Origin* raised when it was published. But he would not have been human if he had not succumbed to the tendency to become infatuated with his own ideas. Add to this the fact that knowledge in his day was nothing like as complete as it is now, and it becomes inevitable that his theory contained some fallacies of principle. One wonders why these fallacies were not shown up long before this; the answer is, they have been, in large measure, but biologists seem to have evolved an ability to ignore them, becoming so wrapped up in their own world, with its great edifice of thought built up by the accumulation of generations of mutually-resonating ideas, that they have now become psychologically incapable of assimilating critical re-thinking of any sort.

This does not only apply to evolutionists. Religious followers seem to be in much the same sort of boat, inescapably enmeshed in long-established doctrine and dogma. I doubt whether either they or the evolutionists will welcome the new amalgam of both views here proposed.

Speaking as an onlooker seeking only truth unbiased by partisan loyalties, and unencumbered with professional axes-to-grind in the fields of biology and theology, it seems to me that this modified theory of evolution provides a credible solution to the bitter conflict which has been raging for decades between Creationists and Evolutionists. The Creationists can retain their belief in a creative Source or Sources, and the Evolutionists can retain *their* belief in the principle of evolution by the natural selection of advantageous variations. And associated with this unexpected possibility of reconciliation between long-standing enemies, is the further possibility that we can at long last cease the practice of misleading our young by inculcating the idea that evolution has done away with the need for a creative source of all existence, with its accompanying

123

implication that religion has been exposed as an out-dated superstition. After all, the fate of the world will soon lie in the hands of the rising generation, and it is a matter of some importance that we cease from inculcating in their still-receptive and questing minds any ideas which lend support to the sort of negative worldview epitomised by Bertrand Russell in the passage quoted on page 4.

CHAPTER XI

IMPLICATIONS

Survival of consciousness. Reincarnation. Religion.

By far the most important of the issues underlying the Creationism/
Evolutionism controversy is unquestionably its overwhelming influence on our philosophy of life. It would be difficult to overstate or
even state adequately, the strength of this influence. Virtually every
member of Western society has been steeped, either consciously or
unconsciously, directly or indirectly, in Darwinian philosophy
almost from infancy. It has unquestionably been a major factor,
some would say *the* major factor, in the decline of religious faith and
values.

As Prof. Berry has said, 'The popular understanding of Darwin is
that he removed God and purpose from the world by making Him
unnecessary as a first cause'.[5] He quotes Sir George Porter,
President of the prestigious Royal Society for the Advancement of
Science: 'Most of our anxieties, problems and unhappinesses today
stem from a lack of purpose which was rare a century ago, and can
fairly be blamed on the consequences of scientific enquiry'.

Anyone who may feel inclined to challenge these views should
refer back to the Bertrand Russell declamation on page 4. This
passage was written in 1903, when at the age of thirty-one Russell
was in the full prime of early manhood, if not perhaps in the prime
of maturity. This declamation illustrates very clearly the potency of

Darwinian thinking to affect the outlook of a highly intelligent man deeply concerned with the problems of existence.

The updated version of evolutionary theory presented in the foregoing pages* eliminates the framework of conjecture and supposition which underlies orthodox evolutionary theory and the negative pessimistic worldview epitomised by Russell, and opens out a way to a positive constructive approach which can be represented by a little plagiarising of Russell:

That man is the product of a transcendental creative Source seeking self-expression; that his origin, his growth, his destiny, are the outcome of a purposive plan of creative design; that no scepticism, no agnosticism, no sophistry, no dialectic, no despair, can prevent the implacable continuance of consciousness beyond the grave; that the vast edifice of human achievement to-date is as nothing compared with the unimaginable vistas of achievement yet to come in the billions of years that lie ahead of the solar system; all these things, if not susceptible to positive proof, are nevertheless so highly probable in the light of practical experience and reasoned argument that no philosophy which denies their truth can hope to satisfy man's deepest aspirations. Only on a strong foundation of unyielding faith in these basic truths can man build for himself a satisfying personal philosophy of life.

Which of these two contrasting views, the negative despair of Russell or the constructive optimism of the revised version, is more concordant with a universe based on the immutable and harmonious laws of nature? Which more likely to lead its adherents to a responsible life of constructive endeavour, and which to a life of apathy, envy, avarice, degeneracy, etc.? As far as I know, Bertrand Russell never recanted his unyielding despair passage, but he did later express very different views, some of which we will encounter shortly.

If Charles Darwin could have been persuaded to consider more sympathetically the suggestion of Asa Grey that the variations acted upon by natural selection might sometimes be caused by the

* See p. 122 in particular.

intervention of God or His delegates, the limitations of his Theory of Evolution could have been removed at a stroke. Its explanatory power would have been enhanced to include all the infinite variety of natural phenomenon, and thus resolve his self-admitted theological muddle (page 116). Such a small price to pay for so great an improvement.

Readers will doubtless have noticed the reference to life after death in Russell's 'unyielding despair' passage and my modified version. This subject may at first sight seem a far cry from evolution, but there is a close connection, inasmuch as the materialistic philosophy inspired by Darwinism and epitomised by Russell, implies that only the physical world of matter is real, all else being mere superstition or self-delusion. Those who subscribe to this view might like to try Coleridge's suggestion of a suspension of disbelief while they ponder the following discussion.

If it *were* true that the physical world of matter is the only reality, then clearly man must cease to exist when his body dies. But if it be true, as I believe I established in Chapter I, that man has two closely-associated complementary aspects, one the objective physical body and brain, the other a subjective non-physical mind or consciousness, then the question arises of what happens to that non-physical aspect when the physical body dies. It is an immutable law of nature that nothing can be utterly destroyed without residue; energy can be converted into matter, and matter into energy, but neither can be annihilated without trace. Nobody can reasonably deny the existence of mental effort, and effort is a form of energy. As Prof. John Morton has observed, however closely the mind may register with the brain, its extinction at physical death would require a greater homogeneity than we have been able to find.[61]

Man is not just another animal, merely one more link in the long chain of biological evolution; he has non-physical qualities such as aspiration, belief, humour, imagination, reason, resolve, which are not the result of biological processes. He has an ego, a psyche, a spirit. He perceives whatever his senses present to him, including his body and sensory organs, so on this count alone he must be something other than the body. He is the perceiver, not the perceived.

If then, man is the culmination of an aeons-long evolutionary process on this planet, a biological life form with added supra-physical qualities, it seems illogical to assume that man's inner spirit will be destroyed before its latent potential comes to fruition. As Dr Leslie Weatherhead remarked, extinction at death would be as irrational as death at birth.[96]

One objection sometimes raised against the idea of survival is that our present life is primarily a matter of *experience*, and since this is directly related to our sensory activities, it follows that experience in any meaningful sense could not occur in the absence of sensory input. This is a fallacy. Experience is not just a passive soaking up of sensory input, it is essentially a matter of interaction between the things that happen to us, and our subjective reactions to them. This active interplay between input and self is not merely physical, it involves the inner self or psyche. Sensory experience is a part of our experience, but it is far from being the most important part, as Helen Keller knew so well.

In fact the apparently real and solid world revealed by our human senses is not really 'real' at all. When the sensory organs are stimulated by events in the external world of nature, electrochemical signals generated at the site of the organ are transmitted to the brain, where they set up a complex dynamic pattern of electrochemical discharges in the neural circuits, and in some totally mysterious manner this neural activity gives rise to conscious perceptions. Our seemingly real 'objective' world of the senses is in fact a subjective world of mental images or constructs. These mental images are the only 'objective reality' we know, or can know. Bertrand Russell observed (truly, this time!) 'There are beliefs, such as the belief that physical objects exactly resemble our sense data, which are entertained until we begin to reflect, but are found to melt away when subjected to close scrutiny'.[69] And the Nobel Laureate, Konrad Lorenz, referred to 'That most mysterious of barriers, utterly impenetrable to human understanding . . . that separates our subjective experience from the verifiable physiological events that occur in our body'.[23] These observations surely present an unshake-able refutation of the materialistic monist philosophy adopted by many scientists and biologists. The interplay of consciousness and brain is irrefutable, self-evident.

Our mental life, our hopes and aspirations, aims and plans, ideas and memories, survives intact despite the ebb and flow of consciousness in sleep or anaesthesia, the unceasing metabolism of the brain, and the unceasing flow of sensations and emotions. We may absorb new ideas as we grow older, but although new perspectives may emerge, at no time do we change into a different person. We remain the same 'me' at seventy as we were at seventeen. Even genetically identical twins know they are separate selves, each a distinctive 'me', however alike physically. So if our consciousness, our subjective inner life of the spirit or essential 'me', continues unhindered throughout all the vicissitudes of physical existence, the unceasing breakdown and rebuilding of all parts of the body and brain, it is illogical to assume that it vanishes without trace when bodily activity finally ceases. As we noted above, *nothing* can be annihilated without residue.

A prima facie objection sometimes raised against the possibility of survival of death, is that even if one accepts the theoretical possibility that an immaterial spirit might be able to survive bodily death, what is there *to* survive when a person has not had the opportunity to develop and retain full personhood, as in the case of a deceased infant, or a senile adult with deranged brain? But these are fallacious questions, since they assume that man is the totality of his physical embodiment and accumulated experience. Clearly, it is only the non-physical part of man that survives, or can survive, bodily death. A damaged or imperfect brain does not imply an imperfect spirit, it only limits the ability of the spirit to manifest fully. So the question is really a *non sequitur*.

Perhaps the strongest argument advanced against the hypothesis of survival of death, is for many people, the allegation that it is wishful thinking. This again is a non-argument, a mere empty sophistry, often a lazy excuse used by those who, for their own reasons, do not give any serious thought to the subject. They are of course entitled to this, but not to use it to dissuade others by implying gullibility. We are too easily scared of being regarded as gullible. The materialist's cynicism can sometimes conceal truth more effectively than can open-minded consideration of logical possibilities. There may be those who accept the hypothesis of survival because they wish it to be true, but while this may prove them to be optimists it does not imply that they are wrong. And conversely, there may be those who accept the alternative of extinction for fear of being misled by emotion, but while this may establish that they are pessimists, it does not imply that they are right. As Arthur Hugh Clough remarked so eloquently 'If hopes are dupes, fears may be liars'. It is not always better to be safe than sorry – you may find yourself being both!

So much, then, in briefest outline, for the logical pros and cons of the case. Much more could be written, but this is not the place to do so, as I am sure many readers will agree! I have concentrated on what I see as the crucial points at issue, and it seems to me that the balance of argument falls fairly and squarely on the side of survival rather than extinction. But this does not prove the case one way or the other. Proof, or final conviction, can come only from evidence, just as in the case of evolution. In the nature of things, evidence of extinction is not available; absence of observable consciousness does not establish annihilation of consciousness, any more than absence of audible speech establishes annihilation of verbal thinking. But in the case of survival, there is a great mass of recorded evidence, much of it vouched for by men and women of undisputed integrity and high intelligence.

Survival evidence falls into several distinct but interlocking categories. One category, that of near-death experiences (NDEs) has the merit of being indubitably first hand. The details and depth of the experience varies from one case to another, but there is a remarkable degree of basic similarity running through all of them, including for instance the feeling of rushing through a long dark tunnel having a bright light at the far end. This part of the NDE was experienced by somebody close to me, a person who had never read about it or heard of it beforehand. There are many books available that deal with the experience fully. One of the best for those new to the subject is Moody's *Life After Life*.[58] Independent corroboration of the experience by medical staff attending a dying patient is not infrequent. In another book *Return From Death*[30] Margot Grey observes 'A critical examination of the details of resuscitative events compared with the medical records and testimony of others present at the time of the NDE seems to suggest that consciousness somehow survives bodily death'. Of course it only establishes short-term survival, but if consciousness survives at all, it would seem illogical to think that it peters out after a lapse of time.

I find it significant that ostensible discarnate communications through mediums or sensitives often report death episodes very similar to NDEs. There is a vast literature dealing with the subject of mediumistic communication, and needless to say, it is riddled with controversy and dispute. But those who have taken the trouble to investigate it thoroughly, usually finish up by becoming convinced by the sheer weight of the evidence, despite initial scepticism. Robert Crookall has listed more than one hundred distinguished people, including world leaders of science, in this category.[15]

One of the most impressive collections of mediumistic evidence is that known as the cross-correspondences. These comprised a lengthy series of scholarly communications spread over a period of thirty years, with fragmentary messages transmitted piecemeal through different mediums working unknown to each other in different parts of the world. The messages made sense only when the separate fragments were brought together at the end of the series. The whole exercise was strongly suggestive of a carefully planned scheme designed to overcome the uncertainties found to occur in normal communications. The method of communication was automatic writing, in which the medium, in mildly dissociated condition, takes dictation from the discarnate communicator. This method eliminates the possibility of telepathic interference from a sitter, an 'explanation' often advanced by sceptics. These cross-correspondences have been thoroughly investigated by experienced researchers, and several books are available for those wishing to consider the affair in more detail.[3]

Of the hundreds of books in this field of mediumistic communication, I find two in particular of considerable significance, Rosemary

Brown's *Immortals At My Elbow*[9] and another by Jane Roberts *The After Death Journal of an American Philosopher*.[76] I think any open-minded person studying Rosemary Brown's book would be impressed with her down-to-earth ordinariness and sincerity. Apart from the communication therein from Einstein as mentioned on page 97, there is a very interesting communication from the discarnate Bertrand Russell. He speaks of a new body which is virtually weightless and very volatile. He can still think and observe and remember, but in greatly enhanced degree. Physical matter now seemed unreal, nothing but a 'seething changing restless sea of indeterminable density and volume'. Time and space are so inextricably interwoven that one begins to see time as a place rather than a sequence or process. The state in which a man exists constitutes the passing reality, which is no longer real after it has passed. The spirit world has a permanence which contrasts strongly with the insubstantiality of the physical world. Earth is a transient world where everything is subject to change and decay, and matter has a deadening effect on mind and spirit. There is a network of thought waves closely connected with the network of electro-magnetic waves of light, heat, radio, etc. It took him a long time to grasp all this, but he is now convinced, with full intellectual understanding, of the existence of God. As a final remark, he wished to tell people that they are far more wonderfully made than they realise; in essence they are gods in the making, although the making has to be their own.

What impresses me about all this is the deep harmony of concepts between the putative Russell and people like Bohm, Fawcett, Eccles, Davidson, etc. Bohm's seminal book was published some years after Rosemary Brown's was written, and in any case it is difficult to believe that it would have fallen within the range of interests of a housewife distinguished only by a gift for music composition. Faced with the need to choose between two possible explanations of the Rosemary Brown book, either a genuine post-mortem communication, or an invention, conscious or unconscious, of Rosemary Brown's mind, it seems to me that the former is the more credible, however much it may conflict with orthodox patterns of thought and belief. Another factor which supports the first explanation is the Russell reference to 'gods in the making'. This is totally at variance with the sentiments expressed in the 'unyielding despair' passage, and with Russell's widely-known passionate atheism during his lifetime. Incidentally, I see a possible connection between these 'gods in the making' and Fawcett's hierarchy of imaginals, (page 103) or G. R. Taylor's forces of which we have as yet no inkling' (page 63).

Jane Robert's book, allegedly a post-mortem report by the American philosopher William James, also bears the stamp of truth within itself. Apart from the essential contents, it contains much frank criticism of James' failings of temperament, which reads more like honest self-criticism than fake criticism invented by a writer who never knew him. The writer describes, openly and freely, the manner in which communications reached her mind, often at inconvenient times as when busy with household chores, and gives an impression of sincerity and integrity.

There are many other books in this field of mediumistic communication, and a few I can recommend unreservedly to open-minded seekers of knowledge are listed in Reference 4. I stress 'open-minded' because many in this cynical age have been influenced to assume that the extraordinary progress of science and technology has exposed religion and survival of death, as outdated superstition, a hangover from olden times when mankind invented a God who intervened in affairs which otherwise seemed inexplicable. Those who hold such views tend to regard all books dealing with esoteric matters as spurious or phoney, nothing but plausible attempts to deceive the gullible. But any genuine book could be rejected on this basis. It simply does not follow that because some books may possibly be spoofs, all are likely to be. The fact that a skilled painter can fake an Old Master so cleverly that it deceives the art experts does not imply that any Old Master may be a fake, and the fact that some esoteric books may be clever spoofs does not imply that all esoteric books are likely to be spoofs. The best way to judge a book is to read it for yourself and then use your own best judgement. If you can compare it with others putting the opposing view, so much the better of course. I am not suggesting that it is unreasonable to adopt a critical analytical approach to the esoteric, only that it is unwise to dismiss it out-of-hand because it might possibly be spurious. Those priding themselves on being down-to-earth realists can sometimes be more seriously misled than those they regard as gullible.

Some words of the psychiatrist Nils Jacobson are relevant: 'Thus instead of one single kind of experience indicating survival, there are several groups of experiences, very different from one another, all of which can be explained harmoniously by the survival hypothesis . . . Each of us must evaluate the material from his own viewpoint, but no-one can do this if he has tossed it aside and dismissed the material as worthless before he begins'.[52]

Before closing this discussion of the hypothesis of survival of death, one aspect of the William James communication merits further consideration, namely his reference to reincarnation. If we accept the possibility that the non-physical indestructible part of man continues after physical death in some other form of existence, this raises the question of whether it existed prior to physical birth. If it continues after bodily death, then logically it should exist before bodily birth. And if it can incarnate once, it can do so again. Thus it seems that the hypothesis of reincarnation follows inevitably from the hypothesis of survival. Schopenhaur once observed that if an Asian were to ask him for a definition of Europe, he would have to answer that 'It is that part of the world which is haunted by the incredible illusion that man was created out of nothing and that his present birth was his first entry into life'.[69]

The doctrine of reincarnation has always been part of the Eastern religions and it is not generally known that it was accepted also by the early Christian Church, until renounced at the 5th Ecumenical Council in A.D. 553.[79]

The doctrine of karma, of the accumulated moral debits and credits incurred during the past incarnations, is an integral part of the doctrine of reincarnation. It is not a question of reward or punishment by a transcendental power, but of self-inflicted cause-and-effect, of reaping whatever we choose to sow. Tennyson expressed it beautifully:

He ever bears about
A silent court of justice in his breast,
Himself the judge and jury, and himself
The prisoner at the bar.

The law of karma is the law of spiritual evolution. Reincarnation is a means of achieving spiritual progress through experience – experience of striving and suffering, of compassion and involvement, in a world of conflict and limitation.

Karma is not necessarily purely personal. F. W. H. Myers spoke of group spirits who nourish a number of individuals, perhaps a dozen or so, perhaps hundreds.[16] Each individual shares in the pooled karma of the group. Myers says this means that most people reincarnate only a few times, obtaining much of their experience by sharing. As Raynor Johnson puts it, we are all linked in a great web of relationships.[45] This aligns with William James' remarks about the inter-connectedness of individual lives.

A practical aspect of life which lends support to the hypothesis of reincarnation is the extraordinarily wide range of human abilities, ranging from saint to scoundrel, savant to simpleton, great art to illiterate scrawl. Physically we are all much the same, apart from deformities, but mentally we vary enormously. This is easier to understand if those who reach the pinnacle of achievement are able to build on a foundation laid down in previous lives. The same thing applies to infant prodigies, when a young child can display an astonishing degree of proficiency in music or mathematics or whatever. And there are occasional cases of marked differences between siblings, even identical twins, which cannot be accounted for by genetic heredity.

A few books dealing with the subject of reincarnation are listed in Ref. 47.

Having passed in a few quick steps from the seeming fallacies of Richard Dawkins and the pseudo-explanations of Maynard Smith and Mark Ridley, to the hypothesis of survival of death, perhaps it would be timely to just 'stand and stare' for a while. Looking back on the preceding pages, I am again struck by the extraordinary variety of people's reactions to Darwinian evolutionary theory. On the one hand we have those like Richard Dawkins, Julian Huxley, Jacques Monod, G. G. Simpson, Philip Kitcher, Michael Ruse, *et al.*, who accept Darwinism unreservedly and promulgate it enthusiastically as established scientific fact replacing the outdated superstition of religious beliefs; and on the other hand there are those like David Watson and the American Fundamentalist Christians, who reject it out of court quite unequivocally, on the grounds of contradicting the Scriptures. Between these two extremes are those who, like Profs Berry and Spanner, manage to accept both Darwinism *and* Christianity, by suitably adjusting their interpretation of the Scriptures. (Of the two, I favour the latter, but go further.) Also there are the non-religious or secular people who are able to see the fallacies inhering in Darwinism irrespective of religious belief. Their ranks include people like G. R. Taylor, Fred Hoyle, Brian Goodwin, Francis Hitchings, Brian Leith, etc. It seems fair to say that the many books written for or against Darwinism tell us more about their authors than about the theory of evolution! As I observed in the Preface, the theory of evolution is usually judged more by the preconceptions of the individual than by the merits or demerits of the theory itself.

I know of no other branch of science which is assessed on this sort of prejudiced, partisan footing. I think the most likely reason for this unusual state of affairs is that Darwin provided, for the first time, a plausible solution to the difficulty many scientists experienced in reconciling the Christian doctrine of creation by a beneficent Creator, with the amount of unmerited suffering to be found in the world of nature. As we noted on page 115 Darwin himself expressed his concern at this. His theory of evolution seemed to provide a plausible answer to this otherwise insoluble problem of evil and suffering in a world created in all its detail by a Divinity, a problem to which the Church itself had no convincing answer.

Seen in this light, it is not surprising that Darwin's theory received immediate acclaim by the scientific fraternity of the day. Doubtless this swift acceptance tended to go to Darwin's head, further softening any residual doubts he may have held about the universal validity of his beloved theory. His disciples unthinkingly accepted Darwin's only real mistake, the unproven *assumption* that the biological variations acted upon by natural selection were necessarily always fortuitous, and in fact took the idea further than Darwin himself intended, to the point of rejecting the whole idea of the intervention of a creative power in the world of nature. This consensus is well illustrated by Julian Huxley's dogmatic assertion that 'Darwinism removed the whole idea of God as the Creator of organisms, from the sphere of rational discussion'.

This enthusiastic indiscriminate acceptance of Darwin's ideas was to become the foundation of a great self-sustaining intellectual edifice of facile thought, much of it essentially supposition and conjecture masquerading as established fact. After all, if you repeatedly affirm as true, that which is really supposition, people come to accept it, and eventually you convince yourself of its truth. This is, I feel sure, the explanation of the many misconceptions to be found in Richard Dawkins' book *The Blind Watchmaker*. In addition to those already dealt with, another major misconception shows up when he accuses Darwin's critics of obtuseness in claiming that natural selection is a matter of chance. Dawkins insists, quite correctly, that natural selection is *non*-random, in that it acts to favour and retain any variations that benefit the organism, and to reject any that are harmful.[19/49] Quite true, but beside the point. Those who claim that evolution is a chance process, do so because evolutionists themselves insist that the variations acted upon by natural selection are purely fortuitous in respect of the welfare of the organism concerned. Natural selection is simply the means by which *variations* are favoured and retained, or rejected and discarded, as the case may be. It is neither random nor directed, but neutral.

I mentioned above the difficulty of obtaining any satisfactory answer from the Churches, to the problem of reconciling the suffering in nature with the religious concept of a loving omnipotent Creator. It was this difficulty, I feel sure, that was the underlying cause of the decline of religious beliefs and values in the century following Darwin's death. Darwin only touched the fringe of the problem when he spoke of the phenomena of parasitism and unconscious cruelty in the animal world. More weighty was the problem of the unmerited suffering and distress inflicted on mankind in this 'dim vast vale of tears', as instanced by the babes born into a life of cruelty and deprivation; the good-living people struck down in their prime by agonising incurable disease; and all the other 'slings and arrows of outrageous fortune'.

The explanation offered by the Churches is that evil and suffering only came into the world when the progenitors of the human race committed the unpardonable sin of disobedience in the Garden. Few people in this age of advanced science and technology feel able to accept the evangelical picture of a vengeful God Who, having created beings with an instinct of curiosity, took revenge on the whole human race for an act of indiscretion perpetrated by their ancestors, and then assigned his own Son to be tortured to death as an act of expiation for this petty crime. (I realise that this may sound somewhat over-simplified, but I think it presents the gist of the teachings.) So it is understandable that this picture should have influenced many people to become disenchanted with religion. It seems to me that in the process of doing so, they have succumbed to the insidious danger of what is euphemistically known as 'throwing out the baby with the bath water'. I suspect they were encouraged in this direction by popular atheistic writers such as Desmond Morris, who blandly informs us that 'God' is merely a modernised version of the ancestral Head Ape,[60] and Robert Ardrey, who writes of 'primitive hunting man's invention' of an all-powerful personal God.[2]

These dogmatic assertions, which I suspect many take as authenticated views of science, are nothing more than personal opinion, just as much as the suppositions and conjectures of evolutionists. Few people are aware that many of the world leaders of science, including the founding fathers of quantum physics, have spoken out strongly in favour of the contrary view. I quote a few:

Einstein. Science without religion is lame, religion without science is blind.
Millikan. A purely materialistic philosophy is the height of unintelligence.

Pasteur. A little science estranges man from God; much science leads him back to God.

Planck. Only those who think by halves become atheists; those who go deep with their thoughts and see the marvellous relationships among universal laws, recognise a creative power.

Lord Kelvin. If you think strongly enough you will be forced by science to believe in God.

Lord Rayleigh. True science and true religion neither are nor could be opposed.

Similar thoughts have been voiced by many others of this calibre, with names such as Bohr, De Broglie, Eddington, Heisenberg, Hoyle, Jeans, Lodge, Newton, Pauli, Sherrington, Schrödinger, J. J. Thompson, Whitehead, etc. It is mostly the lesser lights who favour the atheistic view.

Apart from the outright disbelievers, there are many who prefer to just sit on the fence, adopting the lazy apathetic view that since nobody really *knows* about these things, there is little point in worrying about them. They prefer *not* to seek truth, or to ignore it, should it intrude occasionally. If they could manage it, I suspect they would like to bury their head in the sand at the same time as sitting on the fence! Many of us have a tendency to take it for granted that whatever science pronounces must be true. As Sir John Eccles puts it, the changes in our way of life and thought which have resulted from the advances of science have come to invade aspects of life which have nothing to do with science.[23] And Werner Heisenberg observed that it is only the extension of scientific methods beyond their legitimate field that has led to the deplorable conflict of ideas in the fields of science and religion.

Among the reasons for the continued survival of atheism and materialism is our intellectual laziness, our habit of taking descriptions of how things work as an explanation of their existence. We may read for instance, that the atom resembles a miniature solar system, with electrons orbiting a central nucleus much as planets orbit the sun, and accept this description at face value without stopping to wonder how electrons come into existence, and arrange themselves into a precisely-ordered dynamic structure that is identical for every atom of a given element. Or we read that colour is a component of white light, without pausing to ponder how this came about. Putting a miracle into words seems to blind us to the miracle itself.

Should you begin to wonder what all this has got to do with evolution, it has in my view got a great deal to do with it. Colour is a case very much in point. It has often been said that the obvious survival advantages of colour, as in signalling food, attracting mates, etc., shows that is must have been the outcome of evolutionary processes. As a result of having been exposed for generations to the sloppy thinking of evolutionists as instanced on pages 113–115, this sort of facile uncritical assumption has become part of our unconscious patterns of thought.

Having already proposed a new version of evolution, in which the idea of random variations is extended to include also guided or directed variations, I should perhaps finish the job by taking the liberty of suggesting (only in outline!) a corresponding new version of Christianity. I wait for wrath to descend upon my head!

It may be true that Homo sapiens inherits his physical structure from the animals, but it is equally true that he has supra-physical qualities such as aspiration, compassion, conscience, imagination, resolve, which distinguish him from the animals. He is responsible for his thoughts and actions in a way which no animal ever can be. I find it hard to reconcile this responsibility with the doctrine of vicarious atonement, meaning that our personal wrong-doing can be atoned for by the death of Jesus of Nazareth. This does not mean that I decry in any way the significance of Jesus. On the contrary, I see Him as far and away the best and greatest man who ever lived on earth.

I agree with Raynor Johnson's view that Jesus was unique in that He incarnated, not for His own benefit, but for the benefit of His fellow human beings.[46] I find Him more impressive as a man, than as a member of 'The Holy Trinity', to Whom all things are possible without difficulty presumably. No ordinary man certainly, but one much closer to divinity than ordinary men are. To the best of my admittedly poor knowledge, He never claimed to be God, although He did once say, 'The Father and I are one'. I think He meant this in the sense that any man of the same degree of enlightenment could say it.

Only a very good and very great man could rise to the heights of selfless compassionate love and courage that Jesus rose to. I believe He was enabled to foresee the agonising death that His way of life was to lead to, and calmly went through with it, out of the depths of pure compassion. He, who could have made himself 'Imperator Mundi' had He been so inclined, chose instead the lonely heroic way of total self-sacrifice. 'You could not drink of the cup I drink of.' We think, some of us, of the physical agony He endured, but the mental agony must have been worse. Think how *our* petty little injustices rankle and sting, yet these are as nothing compared to His. He renounced all worldly possessions, even to home and family, endured unprovoked hostility, and 'went about doing good'. He had a most extraordinary capacity for absorbing hostility without becoming hostile. He calmly accepted betrayal by one of His disciples, and denial by another, followed by a mockery of a trial ending in a lingering death of agony at the hands of those He had devoted His short life to. Think, just for a moment, of that awful heart-rending cry, 'My God, my God, why hast thou forsaken me?' Then the final, 'It is accomplished!' Truly He was 'a man of sorrows, and acquainted with grief'. But in the end, anguish was transmuted into glory in the Resurrection. Some will demur at this, and talk of gullibility, but personally I see nothing inherently impossible about the Resurrection, in the light of the many cases of spiritualistic materialisation attested to by people of unimpeachable integrity.[44] As J. B. Phillips has pointed out, the artless matter-of-fact wording of the Gospels and Epistles is very different to what would be expected of a manufactured myth, and carries in its unimbellished simplicity the ring of truth.[71] No story teller would have set down such a naively artless and vulnerable account of events that had never happened.

Some poignant words uttered by the unbreakable Helen Keller reveal a profound truth unknown to those who take the sensory world to be the sole reality: 'To one who is blind and deaf, the spiritual world offers no difficulty'.[87Q] Alexander Pope summed it all up in sublime words:

> All are but parts of one stupendous Whole
> Whose body nature is, and God the soul.

Of course, for all I can prove to the contrary, orthodox Christianity may be right in its teachings, and it may be me, not them, who is barking up the wrong tree. So be it. I do not seek to contradict the doctrines of orthodoxy, nor to influence the beliefs of its followers. I seek only that which appeals to my reason as the most likely to be true; and I suspect that a majority of the rising generation are likely to find this sort of religion more acceptable.

To my mind, the Heavenly Father of the Christian Churches is far too small, a naively anthropomorphic God having human weaknesses and failings. Far greater is the God revealed by a study of the stupendous immensity of the universe and the problem of origins. A God Who in a few days miraculously creates a universe and its teeming life out of nothing, by Divine fiat, is to my mind less credible than a God who, as the Source of an infinite supply of Cosmic Energy forming an enfolded or Implicate Order, causes it to manifest by the action of His immutable laws, as an Explicate Order of matter comprising atoms and their constituent particles formed out of, and sustained in perpetual motion by, the said Energy. Likewise, a God who creates terrestrial life-forms at the same time as the planet which is their home, is less credible than a God who starts by creating primitive life-forms suited to the primitive conditions on a young planet, and endows them with a genetic control system having just sufficient flexibility to accommodate modifications suited to improved conditions on a maturing planet. And a God who, instead of exercising control over the ever-increasing adaptation and complexification of life, leaves it to contingency, is certainly less credible than a God who exercises control by directing the multitudinous small variations permitted by the genetic system He designed for that purpose. And if instead of lumbering Himself with the vast amount of detail work involved, He delegates it to a great army of trained assistants, then that further enhances His credibility in my eyes.

Some eloquent words of Herbert Spencer, a contemporary of Charles Darwin, written a century before David Bohm, are noteworthy:

> Amid the mysteries which become the more mysterious the more they are thought about, there will remain the one absolute certainty, that man is ever in the presence of an Infinite and Eternal ENERGY from which all things proceed.

It is only fair to add here that a powerful case for the compatibility of both orthodox Christianity and orthodox Evolution was put forward by the French palaeontologist and Jesuit priest, Teilhard de Chardin.[12] He combined an unconditional total belief in the doctrines of Roman Catholic Christianity with an equally unconditional total belief in the principle of Darwinian evolution, with no trace of concern for the practical difficulties of either. His best-known book, *The Phenomenon of Man* (published posthumously due to a Churchly interdiction during his lifetime), can perhaps be summarised by saying that he saw evolution as a continuous and inevitable progress towards complexification and its concomitant of consciousness. It started with the alpha of subatomic particles, and continued in uninterrupted succession to atom – molecule – macromolecule – cell – plant – animal – human – reflective or self-aware consciousness, culminating in a unified collectivity of all individual consciousnesses, which he termed Omega. (Alpha and Omega are the first and last letters of the Greek alphabet.) Just as the word 'biosphere' has come into use to represent the biological layer or sphere of living organisms surrounding the earth, so he coined the term 'noosphere' from the Greek *noos*, mind, to represent the layer or sphere of thought. The noosphere culminates in the realm of Omega, the ultimate pinnacle of the spiritual essence of mankind, the unified totality of reflective thought and consciousness, and in some mysterious way the realm of divinity also. Not surprisingly, Sir Julian Huxley, who wrote an Introduction, admitted that he was unable to follow this particular aspect of Père Teilhard's reasoning.

143

The case presented by Teilhard de Chardin is far more weighty than this brief outline may suggest, and those interested in the problem of reconciling doctrinal religion with evolution would do well to read his book for themselves, although admittedly they may not find it easy going. The problems of reconciling Evolution and Christianity are lucidly presented in David Lack's thoughtful and impartial book.[50]

A different concept, which can, I think, be regarded as a physical analogy to de Chardin's spiritual concept of Omega, is Lovelock's hypothesis of Gaia, the earth Goddess.[54] Just as Omega is seen as the unified totality of mental or spiritual activity on the planet, so Gaia can be seen as the unified totality of physical or biological activity and behaviour. Lovelock defines it as the hypothesis that the physical and chemical condition of the terrestrial atmosphere, oceans, and soil, has been brought to, and thereafter maintained in, a healthy state suited to the presence of life, by virtue of a system of informational feedback exercised by life itself. This contrasts with the Darwinian view that life adapted to the environment as both of them evolved in their separate ways.

There are many ways in which this close control of environmental chemistry becomes evident. For instance, the composition of the earth's atmosphere is somehow maintained in a state of severe chemical dis-equilibrium, with the most plentiful ingredient, nitrogen, maintained at 79 per cent, whereas if left to its own chemical devices it would become zero or thereabouts. Oxygen also would be nil in conditions of natural equilibrium, but is in fact held at 21 per cent, a figure which is ideal for life. Carbon dioxide is held down to .03 per cent, whereas it would make up almost all the atmosphere in conditions of chemical equilibrium. Other ingredients such as ammonia, methane, nitrous oxide, and trace compounds such as methyl chloride and methyl iodide, are all held at concentrations suited to life, in violation of chemical equilibrium.

Likewise, the composition of the oceans is maintained at about the optimum proportions for life by some system of informational feedback. For instance, salinity has been held close to its present figure of 3.4 per cent for billions of years, despite the continuous influx of mineral salts from planetary land-rain and river-water, which would double the present salt-content in only 80 million years. An increase of only 1 per cent over the figure of 3.4 per cent would render life as we know it impossible.

Yet a further example of providential control of the environment is the ambient temperature of the atmosphere, which has been maintained at a figure suitable for life despite an increase in the sun's radiation of at least 30 per cent during the 3½ billion years of life's history. If it were not for the informational feedback system, this would have resulted in a climate totally unsuitable for life either late or early in that period.

These are only a few of the numerous examples which Lovelock gives, but they suffice to make the point. It seems abundantly clear that without the influence of an organised control system based on informational feedback, the continuous presence of life on this planet would not have been possible. Control systems do not organise themselves, they are the outcome of purposive intelligence, and this fact seems to validate Lovelock's concept of an intelligent entity Gaia. An alternative explanation can be found in Fawcett's concept of Imaginism referred to above and outlined on pages 102–108. There is no evading the point that *some* form of transcendental intelligence, call it what you will, must have been involved.

Support for this last view is to be found in another contemporary source, Sheldrake's hypothesis of Formative Causation.[81] This hypothesis argues that any biological or physical behaviour which is not directly explicable in terms of a physical cause, can be explained by the influence of intangible 'morphogenetic fields' which, like the known fields of physics such as the magnetic and gravitational fields, are detectable only by their effects. The first time a physical event occurs, it is accompanied by a concurrent morphogenetic field, and whenever the event if repeated thereafter, it is caused to follow the original form by virtue of inter-field resonance – a sort of morphic memory.

Sheldrake quotes many cases which can be best explained by this hypothesis. For instance, after blue-tits acquired the trick of stealing milk by pecking at milk-bottle caps in one locality, the habit quickly spread throughout the blue-tit family in geographically isolated locations throughout the world. Another example is the crystallisation of glycerine; at one time glycerine had never been known to crystallise, and then on one occasion it was found crystallised after a long sea voyage. After that date it began to crystallise with increasing frequency.

Sheldrake's hypothesis seems well supported by evidence, and difficult to refute, but there is one difficulty which I find hard to accept, namely that of accounting for the *first* occurrence of the field. I can accept the phenomenon of immaterial mind or intelligence acting on physical matter, since this happens every time our volition causes bodily movement, but the converse of physical acting on psychical seems much more unlikely. Sheldrake admits the difficulty, but dismisses it on the basis that it is beyond the scope of science. As he observes, the original event can be ascribed either to chance, or to a creative power innate in nature, or to a transcendental creative agency, but there is no way an experiment can demonstrate which is the correct one of these three possibilities. True enough, but that is no excuse for washing our hands of the problem and ignoring it. We can, and should, exercise our best reason and judgement to weigh up which seems the most rational choice. For my part, I find the most reasonable postulate is that of a transcendental creative agency, since as we have seen, this can explain so many of the otherwise intractable problems of the universe.

Reason is one of man's greatest gifts, but unless used properly it can also be one of his greatest weaknesses. It all depends on the premises one starts from. As somebody (I forget the name) once observed, the simplest mind can arrive at a sound conclusion provided it starts off from a sound premise, but the greatest mind can go hopelessly astray if it starts from a faulty one. A case in point is the reasoning of Russell in the passage quoted on page 4. Although the eloquence and self-consistency of this passage may perhaps give a prima facie impression of sound thinking, it is as we have noted, sheer nonsense, simply because Russell based it on the false premise that the universe and its contents are the outcome of purposeless chance. Another case is that of Darwin's *Origin of Species*, which was based on the false premise that the biological variations acted upon by natural selection are necessarily always random in respect of the organism's needs and welfare and survival. Darwin himself did not take this assumption to its logical conclusion, but his disciples were quick to do so, with the results we have seen, as exemplified, for instance, by Julian Huxley and Richard Dawkins among many others.

I shall not be surprised if critics of my book seek to turn the foregoing argument against me, on the grounds that my own premise of the intervention in nature of a transcendent creative power is itself an unproven and indeed unprovable assumption. My answer is that whilst they are quite right, every argument *has* of necessity to be founded on at least one premise, stated or unstated, and this particular premise of mine is the only one fully congruent with the harmonious order and regularity that we find in the universe in which we exist. All anybody can do, is survey the alternative possibilities, and choose whichever one best fits the known facts of the case.

Another point that may be turned against me, is that when I denounce those who promulgate opinion as fact, I do exactly the same thing myself. This is almost the same point as the last one, and has little if any validity. Where I express an opinion, I explain the reasoning on which it is based, and unless anyone can fault my reasoning, they are not entitled to contest the opinion expressed.

One can usually learn more from those who disagree with one, than from those who agree, and it will be interesting to see what real points of disagreement emerge from my critics, of whom there will no doubt be many. I anticipate all sorts of evasion, prevarication, and equivocation, but have little hope of carefully reasoned discussion of the actual arguments and criticisms I have raised. I can only *hope* that I shall be pleasantly surprised!

The only other hope I feel concerned to express, is the far more important one that those concerned with the education of the rising generation will give serious consideration to the points I have made. One thing I do share with the Creationists is their deep concern at the negative influence of inculcation in orthodox evolutionary theory, with its implication of a purposeless universe and ultimately a purposeless life. No price is too big for an ending of this practice.

147

EPILOGUE

It is ironic, to put it mildly, that our fervent evolutionists, our Julian Huxleys, George Simpsons, Phillip Kitchers, Richard Dawkins, et al., while solemnly engaged in extolling the virtues of Darwin's theory of evolution, seem to be unaware that they themselves are each a living demonstration of the gross inadequacies of that much-lauded theory. They fail to realise that their physical bodies, composed of atoms that cannot be accounted for by Darwinism, came into existence through the workings of a reproductive system which cannot by any reasonable stretch of imagination be seen as the outcome of Darwinian processes of the natural selection of random variations.

To understand this, you need only consider *one* of the numerous concurrent requirements of human reproduction, such as the production of male sperm cells having half the normal complement of chromosomes, and provided with a propulsive system *motivated by an insistent urge* to seek out and unite with the female ovum. To anyone giving any serious thought to this essential requirement, it is quite inconceivable that these ingeniously contrived purposively-acting germ-cells could have been the outcome of an accumulation of genetic copying mishaps, let alone all the other requirements at the same time.

The bodies so mysteriously brought into existence include a brain which is itself a miracle of highly-organised complexity beyond Darwinian explanation, together with an associated mind or

148

consciousness likewise beyond Darwinian explanation. And every time they open their eyes they are bombarded with colour sensations which are also beyond Darwinian explanation. Every time they move a limb or laugh, this physical brain reacts to a non-physical thought or emotion.

Darwin seems to have come within touching distance, so to speak, of these difficulties for his theory, when he thought about the botanical origin of the angiosperms or flowering plants, which reduced him to the peevish complaint that this was 'an abominable mystery'. He either failed to recognise, or turned a blind eye to, the fairly obvious fact that the biological origin of the mammalian reproductive system presented an even more intractable problem for his theory. And clearly, the problem is not confined to mammalian reproduction, but applies universally to *all* life forms, whether vegetable or animal, alga or bacterium, hollyhock or hominid. Not even the most fanatical evolutionist would go so far as to claim that a reproductive system, however crude, evolved during the breeding lifetime of the first member of a radically new life form!

Darwin and his disciples seem to exemplify, doubtless quite unconsciously, Thomas Gray's famous aphorism '. . . where ignorance is bliss, 'Tis folly to be wise'. Maybe a good motto for those seeking a complacent peace of mind, but not for those seeking truth! I am reminded of Lewis Carroll's Red Queen, who mystified poor Alice by boasting that she sometimes managed to believe as many as six impossible things before breakfast. The RQ would have been mortified to find that evolutionists could beat her at her own game!

Should any readers find all this puts a strain on their credulity, as well it might, I can only suggest they should refer back to pages 18–22, 46–48, 50–54, 97–98, 119–122, and endeavour to find a flaw or fallacy in the arguments there advanced.

Despite the irrefutability of the facts here presented, I suspect that it may prove impossible to convince contemporary evolutionists and educationists of the fallacies in the doctrines they are enthusiastically spreading to all who will listen or have to listen. The distinguished physicist Max Planck once observed that a new truth does not usually triumph by converting its adversaries, but by virtue of the fact that the adversaries eventually die off and are replaced by a new generation who grow up familiar with the new truth. And Sir Donald Tovey is quoted in one of Rosemary Brown's fascinating books[10] as saying that many minds in our world are deeply encrusted in crystallised concepts which cause those affected to fondly imagine that their beliefs are infallible. He added that despite the dangers of over-credulity, those regarded as credulous were more likely to be receptive to truth than were critics and cynics.

The more I ponder this astonishing situation, the more incredible I find it. There cannot be, I feel sure, another discipline in the whole of science whose practitioners become so besotted with its doctrines as to lose completely their capacity for critical examination of any deficiencies or fallacies therein. Some scientists tend to regard religious believers as over-credulous and gullible to the point of freely accepting fairy tales, but it seems to me that there are as many fairy tales in evolutionary literature as there are in the Gospels. Something more potent than mere habits of thought must be involved in seeking an answer to this ironic situation, surely. Perhaps it lies in the direction of Rupert Sheldrake's idea of self-reinforcing mutually-resonating fields of influence already mentioned on page 145, but I must leave it to the experts, the psychologists and psychiatrists, I suppose.

Let's try to finish on a more positive note! Gordon Taylor's thoughtful book on the mystery of evolution concludes with the remark 'Recognition of the probability that there are forces at work in the universe of which we have as yet scarcely an inkling . . . is a step towards the freeing of the human mind which is pregnant with promise'.[89] Once we have broken free from our long enslavement in the stifling dogmas of crystallised orthodoxy, we can open our minds to the luxury of unrestricted thought about that stupendous whole 'whose body nature is, and God the soul'. No longer need we shy away from reasoned speculation about the possibility of consciousness continuing in some form of after-death existence. No longer need we fear the charge of gullibility if we decide that the existence of a transcendental creative agency is a reasonable possibility. Away with despair and negativity, on with hope and optimism! For too long our minds have been dulled by specious talk of randomness and chance, and our hopes mocked by mediocre men incapable of breaking away from long-standing doctrines. The time is surely ripe for the pregnant promise foreseen by Gordon Taylor to come full term to fruition.

As Alfred North Whitehead observed,[28] it is easy to devise self-consistent but false theories, provided you are content to disregard half the evidence; but the only way to avoid the fluctuating extremes of fashionable opinion is an unflinching determination to take the whole of the evidence into account, whatever the cost. And his penetrating definition of religion is worthy of note:

> Religion is the vision of something which stands beyond, behind, and within the passing flux of immediate things, something which is real, and yet waiting to be realised; something which is a remote possibility, and yet the greatest of present facts; something which gives meaning to all that passes, and yet eludes apprehension; something which is the final ideal, and yet the hopeless quest; something whose possession is the final good, and is yet beyond reach.

As Hoyle has observed, it almost seems that mankind has been provided with a congenital compulsion to believe in a transcendental creative agency beyond the everyday world of nature.[41] Seen in this light, the views we have found to be associated with names such as Bohm, Davidson, Eccles, Evans, Fawcett, Hoyle, Lovelock, Lorenz, Planck, Sheldrake, Schopenhaur, Taylor, Walker, Wheeler, represent partial truths extracted from the infinite well of universal truth in an attempt to fill the aching void left by the Evolutionist's dismissal of God and the general decline in spiritual values.

I hope that my earlier advice to 'bear with me' will now be found justified!

In conclusion, perhaps I may quote a few verses which I find apt, without stirring up further controversy. I envy those who have such mastery of the language as enables them to express in a few eloquent words, the essence of life's deepest problems.

151

I keep six honest serving men
  (They taught me all I knew);
Their names are What and Why and When
  And How and Where and Who.

Rudyard Kipling

If fallacies come knocking at my door,
I'd rather feed and shelter full a score,
Than hide behind the black portcullis, doubt,
And run the risk of barring one Truth out.

Ella Wheeler Wilcox, Credulity

So many Gods, so many creeds,
  So many paths that wind and wind,
While just the art of being kind
  Is all the sad world needs.

Ella Wheeler Wilcox, The World's Need

Let there be many windows to your soul,
That all the glory of the universe
May beautify it. Not the narrow pane
Of one poor creed can catch the radiant rays
That shine from countless sources. Tear away
The blinds of superstition; let the light
Pour through fair windows broad as Truth itself
And high as God.

                Why should the spirit peer
Through some priest-curtained orifice, and grope
Along dim corridors of doubt, when all
The splendour from unfathomed seas of space
Might bathe it with the golden waves of Love?
Sweep up the débris of decaying faiths;
Sweep down the cobwebs of worn-out beliefs,
And throw your soul open to the light
Of Reason and of Knowledge.

Ella Wheeler Wilcox, Progress

I hold that when a person dies,
His soul returns again to earth;
Arrayed in some new flesh disguise
Another mother gives him birth.
With sturdier limbs and brighter brain
The old soul takes the road again.

                              John Masefield.

Our birth is but a sleep and a forgetting;
    The Soul that rises with us, our life's Star,
Hath had elsewhere its setting
    And cometh from afar.
                    William Wordworth, *Intimations of Immortality*

                        And I have felt
A presence that disturbs me with the joy
Of elevated thoughts; a sense sublime
Of something far more deeply interfused,
Whose dwelling is the light of setting suns,
And the round ocean and the living air,
And the blue sky, and in the mind of man.
                         William Wordsworth,
            Lines composed a few miles above Tintern Abbey

A fire-mist and a planet,
    A crystal and a cell,
A jelly fish and a saurian,
    And caves where the cave-men dwell;
Then a sense of law and beauty,
    And a face turned from the clod –
Some call it Evolution,
And others call it God.
                W. H. Carruth, *Each in his own tongue*

    To strive, to seek, to find, and not to yield.
                    Alfred, Lord Tennyson, *Ulysses*

The race is divided into two classes, those who go ahead
and do something, and those who sit still and inquire
'Why wasn't it done the other way?'

Oliver Wendell Holmes

The foolish and the dead alone never change their opinion.

James Russell Lowell

Say could aught else content thee? Which were best
After so brief a battle, an endless rest,
Or the ancient conflict rather to renew,
By the old deeds strengthened, mightier deeds to do?

F. W. II. Myers

POSTSCRIPT

Since writing the foregoing pages, I have had sight of a recent new book, *Science of the Gods*,[100] which throws an intriguing new light on many of the points I make. The authors, Ash and Hewett, seek to revive and modernise the famous vortex theory of Lord Kelvin, a theory strongly backed by such leading figures of the scientific world as Helmholtz, Clerk Maxwell, J. J. Thomson, etc. This theory postulated that the atom is a vortex in the ether; but the ether hypothesis has long since been discarded, and the atom is now known to be a dynamic structure of subatomic particles. The Ash and Hewett book presents a revised version of Kelvin's theory, with the ether replaced by energy, and the *subatomic particles* seen as vortices of energy.

It might be objected that whilst a vortex in a material substance such as a gas or a liquid is a known phenomenon, a vortex of immaterial energy is something of a contradiction in terms, an abstract concept which cannot be taken as a practical possibility. But this objection is certainly debatable; light is now regarded as a wave motion of electromagnetic energy, and if energy can take the form of a wave, we can hardly argue that it cannot take the form of a vortex. In fact this modernised vortex theory is strongly supported by the modern concept of elementary particles as condensations of energy, 'regions of an energy field where the field density is enormously high' (page 18). It is hard to understand how specks of condensed energy could form and hold that form indefinitely, but this difficulty is lessened if the specks are seen as tightly-wound spherical vortices or whirling balls of energy.

Ash and Hewett point out that the revised hypothesis can account for some of the mysteries of quantum physics, such for instance as the 'spin' of elementary particles, which although not a simple matter of bodily rotation, is nevertheless regarded as an intrinsic property of the particle.

And they suggest a radically new concept of space as a property of energy; they postulate that the vortices of energy which form the particles of matter, should be regarded not as defined specks of finite size, but as 'bubbles' of dynamic energy having a very dense core surrounded by a vastly-extended peripheral region of the rarified outer swirls of energy. The very dense central core which forms the elementary particle of matter, is surrounded by a vast outer region of highly rarified energy which forms the 'space' separating physical objects. The boundary of the matter vortex is established by the degree of density which our senses and instruments are able to respond to; everything within this boundary is 'matter', and everything outside the boundary is 'space'.

The authors suggest also that time is related to the vortex. Time is measured in terms of the cyclic frequency of recurrent physical events, our everyday time being measured in terms of rotation of the earth around the sun, and about its own axis. Scientists think in terms of atomic time, and the vortex spin may well be the most basic measure of time, the ultimate 'atomic clock'.

These ideas of Ash and Hewett accord remarkably well with Einstein's insight into the relationship of matter and energy as expressed by his famous equation $E = MC^2$, and also with his postulate that space and time are interconnected.

A further proposal is associated with Einstein's finding that the velocity of light is an absolute constant of nature, which can never be exceeded or reduced. Light always travels at exactly the same velocity of 300,000 km per second (in vacuo) irrespective of the speed of an observer moving towards or away from the source of light. To anything moving at the speed of light, time and mass expand to infinity, and space collapses to zero. Thus the velocity of light (usually denoted by the symbol C) is a critical boundary condition of the universe in which we live. Ash and Hewett postulate that this critical limiting velocity C is the speed of movement in the vortex, thus accounting very simply for the close links between energy, mass, and light.

They go on to moot the further possibility that this velocity of the vortices of matter could conceivably be increased in other realms of existence, since there seems to be no *a priori* reason why pure movement must always be restricted to some particular value. If for instance the vortex speed were to be increased to say 2C, then objects although of the same form as in our physical world, would be unperceivable to our human senses and instruments. They would vanish from our ken, but might have reality in some other realm of existence, a super-physical realm of super-matter and super-energy. This proposal offers a possible explanation of the many cases of near-death experience, mediumistic communication, etc, referred to on pages 130–134.

And from the evolutionary viewpoint, it offers an intelligible explanation of the means by which a transcendental creative intelligence could operate to bring about the advantageous variations of biological structure which are beyond the probability of fortuitous contingency. The 'life fields' of Sheldrake, Burr, Evans, et al. (page 100) could act upon the DNA coils of the chromosomes and genes by resonating with the electromagnetic properties of the coils. They might act either to determine which sections of the DNA sequences are used, or by modifying the code itself. And obviously they could provide the means by which the proteins constructed by the code are built into the various structures and organs of the growing embryo (pages 9 and 109). This could account also for the very high degree of reproductive accuracy achieved by the genetic system, and for the *rarity* of mutations (pages 29 and 60).

The plain fact that all elementary particles of any particular type such as electrons, or protons, are identical, is consistent with the view that they are the creation of a single omnipotent source, and is hard to explain on any other basis.

It is significant that Ash and Hewett see God as pure consciousness bringing the vortices of matter into existence by an act of conscious imagination, a concept which harmonises with Fawcett's philosophy of Imaginism outlined on pages 102–107 above. And they see consciousness as the source of energy, a concept which harmonises with the view expressed on page 14 that energy is an emanation or outflowing of God. As pure consciousness, God has no form, and can manifest only through His creation, which is brought into existence by an act of conscious imagination 'backed by intelligence, impelled by will and activated by love'. What He gets out of it is experience – the experience of all created things, from a blade of grass to a thinking being.

If the sustained act of imagination which creates and sustains in existence the vast universe and its teeming contents were to cease even for a moment, everything in the universe would disappear in a flash, reverting to the primal undifferentiated energy which underlies it all.

If consciousness and energy are the fundamental realities, then they must be present in some degree in all creation, from elementary particle to human brain, from mineral to plant to animal. What a vision to stagger the human imagination – God present in each atom of the body – a God infinitely greater and closer than the father figure of the Scriptures. Tennyson's lines 'Closer is He than breathing, Nearer than hands and feet' become not just poetic metaphor, but living truth.

It is fascinating to find Ash and Hewett using exactly the same words used by Bertrand Russell (page 132) 'We are gods in the making'. The gods are of course not God, but highly-evolved being having some degree of the attributes of God. If we are indeed gods in the making, then we can see ourselves as in the kindergarten stage of an immensely long process of learning and growing, a process which will eventuate in some far-distant time in a realm of joyful creativity. It seems unreasonable to assume that this destiny could be achieved in one terrestrial lifetime.

It is interesting to find this deep accord between two contemporary writers and the earlier writers we have discussed in the foregoing pages. Clearly the names of Ash and Hewett can be added to the list (page 151) of those who have dipped into the well of universal truth.

Another book bearing on my Chapter VIII, is *Superforce*[101] by the astrophysicist Paul Davies. This book provides a dramatic picture of the extraordinary lengths to which scientists will go, in attempting to explain the origin of the universe in purely physical terms. The theory propounded by Prof. Davies is too technical to expound in these pages, but the high spots can be outlined by saying that the universe is said to have begun its existence as an infinitesimal 'bubble' of vacuum about a billionth of a trillionth of a millimetre in diameter. The quantum fields in this unimaginably tiny vacuum bubble came spontaneously into an 'excited' condition accompanied by an enormous explosive force causing the bubble to expand at trillions of times the velocity of light.

After the lapse of an infinitesimal moment of time, an unimaginable billionth of a trillionth of a trillionth of a second, this tiny bubble had increased its size a trillion-trillion fold; and by the end of the first second it had expanded to ten light years in diameter.

(It is easy to write of billionths and trillionths of a second, but hard to grasp the practical meaning of the words. Consider the matter of shutter speeds in photography: the shortest exposure available with a costly large-aperture lens is likely to be $1/1000$ of a second. Imagine now a thousandth of *this* very brief time, and you have a millionth of a second; then take a millionth of this millionth, and you have trillionth of a second. You can see why I used the adjective 'unimaginable'!).

In this first 10^{-33} second of hyper-inflation while the vacuum was in the 'excited' condition, it developed spontaneously an unimaginably enormous amount of energy, and this prodigious self-generated energy was the source of all the untold trillions of stars and galaxies in the present-day universe.

This exotic scenario flatly contradicts two of the basic tenets of science, firstly that nothing can travel faster than light, since it would require infinite energy to accelerate anything up to, let alone beyond, this limiting velocity; and secondly the law of conservation of energy, which states that whilst energy can change its form, it can never be destroyed without remainder, or created out of nothing. No exception to these two fundamental laws of nature has ever been found throughout the whole history of science. Yet so deep is the conviction of scientists that *everything* must have a physical explanation that they are prepared to accept exceptions to their own experience rather than admit the possibility of a transcendental influence in nature. Davies does admit that the whole approach is speculative, and Alan Guth, the inventor of the 'inflationery' hyper-inflation hypothesis, acknowledges that it is speculation piled on speculation, or speculation squared to use his expression. Speaking as an engineer, I think it could be regarded as a 'Fantasia Mathematica' of a high order.

Another aspect of the fantasy is the hypothesis that space was originally ten-dimensional, and that seven of these dimensions became 'rolled up' and enfolded in our familiar three-dimensional space, thereby releasing the enormous repulsive force which powered the hyper-expansion phase of the Big Bang. There was no 'force', only seven rolled-up dimensions of space.

Another interesting point Davies makes is that anyone uncomfortable with the idea of self-generated energy can fall back on the 'zero-total-energy' argument which I criticised on page 86. But he adds the proviso that this alternative should not be taken *too* seriously, since 'the whole concept of energy is of dubious status as far as gravity is concerned', which I take to be another way of saying what I said on page 86.

Yet a further aspect of the scenario is the hypothesis that at the end of the inflationary hyper-expansion phase, the universe was filled with a broth of extraordinarily heavy particles packed to a density of a trillion trillion trillion trillion trillion (10^{60}) tons per cubic millimetre, a mere pinhead. *Extraordinary* seems the right word!

I find it remarkable that after expounding these mathematical gymnastics purporting to demonstrate how the universe created itself, Prof. Davies finds himself forced to the conclusion that the presence of so much order in the universe, with everything inter-related by precisely controlled fundamental constants and laws, cannot have been the outcome of blind chance, and can only be reasonably explained as the outcome of an underlying purposive power of extraordinary ingenuity and cleverness. He makes the point that 'because science presupposes rational laws, the scientist rarely stops to think about why these laws exist'. His final sentence reads 'If physics is the product of design, the universe must have a purpose, and the evidence of modern physics suggests strongly to me that the purpose includes us'.

I find it encouraging that at least one eminent theoretical physicist should arrive (by an even more circuitous route) at the opposite conclusion to that of others such as Heinz Pagels and Stephen Hawking. Having done so, it only remains to replace the decidedly *un*scientific and quite untestable hypothesis of self-generated energy by the more credible postulate of energy being an emanation or essence of the creative Power. After all, as Davies himself admits, energy is an abstract concept which has become so much a part of our everyday vocabulary that we embue it with concrete existence.

One more book I *must* mention is Stephen Gould's much-praised *Wonderful Life*, which to my mind provides (quite unconsciously and certainly unintentionally), an outstanding demonstration of the overriding impact of dogma on scientific thought.[103]

Science tells us that the earth came into existence 4,800 million years ago, and after a cooling-off period of 700 million years, simple unicellular life arose, such as blue-green algae, diatoms and bacteria, based on primitive prokaryotic cells lacking a nucleus, mitochondria, and chromosomes etc. The remnants of this primeval life can be found in the form of stromatolites, mounds of layered sediment trapped and bound by prokaryotic cells.

This tranquil scene continued uninterruptedly for 2,400 million years, when a more advanced type of cell, the eukaryotic cell having a nucleus with chromosomes, etc., appeared. But despite the multicellular potential of this new cell, single-celled life continued uneventfully for a further 700 million years, in the form of amoeba and paramecium etc. Only after this long delay did multi-celled life appear, in the form of flat soft mats, quilts and pancakes, followed by tiny reef-building shelled animals. These primitive species are known as the Ediacara and Tommotian fauna.

Then quite suddenly, within the geological blink of an eye, there came a great outburst of complex multicellular animals with hard parts. This unprecedented 100-million-year outburst is known to biologists as the Cambrian explosion, since it marks the beginning of the Cambrian Period some 600 million years ago. A rich fossil record of this dynamic outburst has been found in the Burgess Shale in a quarry located at an altitude of 8000 feet in the Canadian Rockies, and it is this fossil record that provides the background of Prof. Gould's fascinating book.

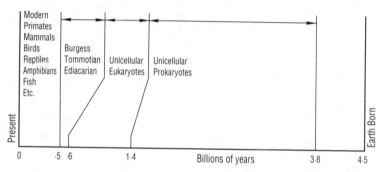

Quoting Gould, these 'weird and wonderful' animals display an amazing array of anatomical constructions, including for example one with stilts, one with a sort of everted circular saw for a mouth, another with seven eyes, and so on. In all there are several dozen different types, of which only four are regarded as ancestral to later types. 'With far fewer species, the Burgess Shale contains a disparity in anatomical design far exceeding the modern range throughout the world.' Sites similar to the Burgess have been found in other parts of the world, including Germany, Greenland, Australia and China, establishing that the Burgess is representative of a world-wide phenomena.

Thus we have an extended period of primordial unicellular life in a state of stagnation for 3,200 million years, followed by an explosion of sophisticated life forms in an amazing variety of anatomical constructions, involving segmented bodies, jointed legs, gills, mouths and feeding appendages, antennae, eyes, some sort of sensory and nerve ganglia to provide awareness of food and

162

predators, plus some sort of reproductive system including gameto-genital organs etc. The big question is, how did these animals originate?

The essence of Darwinism is that all life evolved by the automatic adoption of whatever advantageous variations of structure happened to become available to the earlier forms. It is straining credulity beyond all reasonable limits to say that the Burgess animals evolved from the unicellular life of the Precambrian era, by adopting whatever advantageous variations happened to occur in that unicellular life.

Nor do the intermediate forms of simple Edicarian and Tom-motian fauna help – in fact it is thought that these probably died out without leaving descendants.

Gould quotes the 19th century geologist Sir Roderick Murchison 'The earliest signs of living things [in the Cambrian period], announcing as they do a high complexity of organisation, entirely exclude the hypothesis of a transmutation from lower to higher grades of being.' Sir Roderick saw the Cambrian explosion as indisputable evidence of creation. Darwin realised that this situation presented a major difficulty for his theory, saying 'The case at present must remain inexplicable, and may be truly urged as a valid argument against the views here entertained'. But he stuck to his evolutionary guns, on the grounds that the very incomplete fossil record might be filled in at a later date.

To a considerable extent it has been, by the Burgess Shale and allied finds, but as Gould admits, the situation has now become even more difficult for Darwinian views. If Darwin were to be proved right, we should need, not a wide diversity of forms unrelated to present-day life, but a few forms directly related to the present-day forms, with numerous intermediate forms linking back to the Precambrian forms. I believe that if Darwin could have known of the Burgess Shale fossils, he would have been persuaded that his theory *was* invalidated thereby.

To my mind the Burgess phenomenon is evocative of a Research and Development group staffed by a number of senior designers, each with their own team of detailers, and each given a free hand to develop their own version of a product to meet a given overall plan.

If Douglas Fawcett could have known of the Burgess fossils, I think he would have seen it as the perfect setting for his philosophy of Imaginism. The words 'joy of creation' seem apposite.

With hindsight one sees very clearly that the bitter quarrel between Creationists and Evolutionists was an inevitable outcome of the persistence of two mutually conflicting belief systems.

On the one hand we have the Creationists, deeply immured in centuries-old Christian doctrines founded on Hebrew folk-lore and legend embracing a miraculous *ex nihilo* Creation, a mere few thousand years ago, of the universe and all its contents; the instantaneous creation of the first man and the first woman; the advent of evil and suffering as punishment for the 'sin' of disobedience by these progenitors of the human race; and so on.

And on the other hand we have the Evolutionists, deeply immured in Darwinian doctrines founded on the notion that all the infinite variety of life and behaviour evolved from simpler beginnings, by an automatic process of adopting whatever favourable variations of structure happened by a stroke of luck to become available over extended periods of time embracing millions of generations.

Neither of these mutually-exclusive doctrines was wrong in the context of the times in which they originated. The founding fathers of the Christian Church knew nothing of the stupendous immensity of the universe, or of the geological history of the third planet from the sun, with its glacial ages, continental drift, upthrusting of mountain ranges, petrified forests, extinct dinosaurs and pterodac-tyls, etc. Nor had they any inkling of the prodigious primal energies underlying the manifest physical matter of the universe. They could think and speak only in the context of their times, with the earth seen as the centre of the universe, and man as the pinnacle of creation.

Similarly, in Darwin's day, when science was beginning to expose the irrationality of literally translated Biblical myths and legends, there was little understanding of the complexities of the human brain and its associated sensory organs, and its ability to convert its physical activity into non-physical thoughts and sensations and consciousness. The theory of Evolution appeared to offer a plausible explanation of the phenomena of life in practical terms avoiding the intractable problems of creation by a loving all-powerful deity.

Thus we arrived at a seemingly unresolvable quandary offering a choice of two conflicting philosophies of life, one postulating an omnipotent deity who miraculously created, a mere few millennia ago, everything now in existence – a deity defined in terms of infinite love, wisdom and power, yet fashioned in an anthropomorphic mould embracing human characteristics and weaknesses; and the other postulating that everything now in existence evolved from simpler beginnings by adopting whatever advantageous variations of structure happened by good fortune to become available over hundreds or thousands of millennia. If either of these philosophies is correct, then clearly the other must be wrong. Both were acceptable in their day, but both have succumbed to the ever-growing knowledge of the nature of the universe and its teeming life.

It is perhaps asking too much of human nature to expect the two camps to agree to an amalgamation of views as proposed in the foregoing pages, and it may be that the best we can hope for is that a new generation will grow up sufficiently free from scientific and religious dogma to render the new amalgam acceptable. It is the author's sincere hope that this at least will prove to be the case, and that the educational establishment will prove sufficiently flexible to adopt the new thinking involved. It is high time evolutionary theory evolved a higher degree of clear-headed rationality!

REFERENCES

Note: References marked Q in text mean 'quoted in'.
References with stroke number in text indicate page number,
for instance 19/60 means page 60 of reference 19

1. Ardrey, Robert. *African Genesis*, Collins, 1961...46
2. Ardrey, Robert. *The Hunting Hypothesis*, Futura,
   1976...138
3. Beard, Paul. *Survival of Death*, Pilgrim Books, 1966
   Gauld, Alan. *Mediumship & Survival*, Heinemann, 1982
   Inglis, Brian. *Science & Parascience*, Hodder, 1984   }131
   Lund, David. *Death & Consciousness*, McFarlane,
   1985
4. Beard, Paul. *Living On*, Pilgrim Books, 1980
   Lorimer, David. *Survival?*, RKP, 1984
   Smith, Lester. *Our Last Adventure*, TPH, 1985   }133
   plus those in reference 3
5. Berry, R. J. *God & Evolution*, Hodder, 1988...57, 73, 125
6. The Biblical Creation Society
   50 Brecon Ave, Cosham, Portsmouth, PO6 2AW...73
7. Bohm, David. *Wholeness & the Implicate Order*, RKP,
   1980...19, 105
8. Bohm & Peat. *Science, Order & Creativity*, RKP, 1989...87,
   105
9. Brown, Rosemary. *Immortals At My Elbow*, Bachman &
   Turner, 1974...97, 131

166

10. Brown, Rosemary. *Unfinished Symphonies*, Souvenir Press, 1971...150
11. Capra, Fritjof. *The Tao of Physics*, Fontana, 1976...18
12. Chardin, Teilhard de. *The Phenomenon of Man*, Collins, 1959/63...143
13. Conklin, E. G. *Man Real & Ideal*, p. 147...3
14. The Creation Science Society, P.O. Box 22, Rugby, Warwickshire, CV22 7SY...73
15. Crookall, Robert. *Intimations of Immortality*, James Clark, 1965...131
16. Cummins, Geraldine. *The Road to Immortality*, Pilgrim Books...135
17. Darwin, Charles. *Life & Letters*, ed F. Darwin, c 1902...115, 119
18. Davidson, John. *The Secret of the Creative Vacuum*, C. W. Daniels, 1989...19, 63, 87, 90
19. Dawkins, Richard. *The Blind Watchmaker*, Longman, 1986...24, 25, 28, 29, 31, 35, 43, 52, 69, 82, 114, 121, 127
20. Dewar, Douglas. *The Transformist Illusion*, USA, 1957...44
21. Eccles, John. *Evolution of the Brain: Creation of the Self*, RKP, 1989...101
22. Eccles, John. *The Human Mystery*, RKP, 1984...119, 120, 122
23. Eccles & Robinson. *The Wonder of Being Human*, New Science Library, 1984...2, 21, 128, 139
24. Einstein, Albert. *Ideas & Opinions*, ed Carl Seelig, Souvenir Press, 1954...23
25. Emboden, W. *Bizarre Plants*, Studio Vista, 1974...49
26. Evans, John. *Mind, Body & Electromagnetism*, Element Books, 1986...54, 100, 101
27. Fawcett, Douglas. *Oberland Dialogues* and *Zermatt Dialogues*...102
28. Gardner, Martin, ed. *The Sacred Beetle*, OUP, 1985...151
29. Goodwin, Brian. *Rumbling the Replicator*, Scientific & Medical Network Newsletter 34...35, 100, 109
30. Grey, Margot. *Return from Death*, RKP, 1985...131

31. Haldane, J. B. S. *Possible Worlds*, 1940...23
32. Harman, Willis. *Global Mind Change*, USA, Knowledge Systems, 1988...55
33. Harrison, Edward. *Cosmology*, Cambridge University Press, 1982...84
34. Hawking, Steven. *A Brief History of Time*, Bantam, 1988...86
35. Hayward, Alan. *God Is*, Marshall Morgan & Scott, 1978/9...49, 69, 114
36. Heisenberg, Born, Schrödinger, Auger. *On Modern Physics*, Blond, 1961...19
37. Hilger. *Concise Encyclopaedia of Astronomy*, 1976...83
38. Hitchings, Francis. *The Neck of the Giraffe*, Pan Books, 1982...72
39. Holdroyd, D. R. *Darwinian Impacts*, OUP, 1980...1, 111
40. Hoyle, Fred. *The Intelligent Universe*, Michael Joseph, 1983...42
41. Hoyle & Wickramasinge. *Cosmic Life Force*, Dent, 1988...151
42. Hoyle & Wickramasinge. *Evolution from Space*, Dent, 1981...43
43. Huxley, Julian. *Evolution as Process*, Allen & Unwin, 1954/58 ...115
44. Inglis, Brian. *Science & Parascience*, Hodder, 1984...141
45. Johnson, Raynor. *The Imprisoned Splendour*, Pilgrim Books, 1953/1989...135
46. Johnson, Raynor. *Nurslings of Immortality*, Hodder, 1957–67 ...103, 104, 140
47. Johnson, Raynor. *Light of All Life*, Pilgrim Books, 1984
    Walker, Benjamin. *Masks of the Soul*, Wellingborough, 1981
    Martin & Ebor. *Reincarnation in the 20th Century*, N.Y., 1969 }135
    Stevenson, Ian. *20 Cases Suggestive of Reincarnation*, USA, 1966
    Leggett & Payne, *A Forgotten Truth*, Pilgrim Books, 1986

48. Kitcher, Phillip. *The Case Against Creationism*, OUP, 1982...29, 66, 108, 113, 121
49. Khursheed, Anjam. *Science & Religion*, One World Publishers, 1987...84
50. Lack, David. *Evolutionary Theory & Christian Belief*, Methuen, 1961...144
51. Leith, Brian. *The Descent of Darwin*, Collins, 1982...3, 87, 112
52. Lorimer, David. *Survival*, RKP, 1984...134
53. Lovell, Bernard. *In the Centre of Immensities*, Hutchison, 1979...84
54. Lovelock, James. *Gaia*, Oxford University Press, 1979/89 ...144
55. Mayr, Ernst. *Animal Species & Evolution*, Harvard University, 1963...57, 59, 62
56. May, Robert, and Gallant, Roy, in Reference 59...66
57. Monod, Jacques. *Chance & Necessity*, Fontana...68, 114
58. Moody, R. A. *Life After Life*, Corgi Books, 1977...130
59. Montagu, Ashley, ed. *Science & Creationism*, Oxford University Press, 1984...7, 58, 65, 68, 69, 114, 115
60. Morris, Desmond. *The Naked Ape*, Cape...138
61. Morton, John. *Man, Science & God*, Collins, 1972...127
62. Murchie, Guy. *The Seven Mysteries of Life*, Rider, 1978...48, 57
63. *Nature*, 239, 1972, p. 420...3
64. *Nature*, 218, 1968, p. 527...3
65. *Nature*, Nov. 1968, p. 170...2
66. *Nature*, Vol. 324, Nov. 1986...37
67. *New Scientist*, Vol. 93, No. 1290, 1982...101
68. *New Scientist*, 11 Dec. 1986...114
69. Osborn, Arthur. *The Expansion of Awareness*, TPH, 1955/70 ...128, 134
70. Pagels, Heinz. *The Cosmic Code*, Michael Joseph, 1983...85, 97
71. Phillips, J. B. *The Ring of Truth*...141
72. Prigogine & Stenger. *Order Out of Chaos*, Collins, 1984...44

73. Rawlings, Maurice. *Beyond Death's Door*, Nashville, 1979
74. Ridley, Mark. *The Problems of Evolution*, OUP, 1985...57, 61, 114
75. Rifkin, Jeremy. *Algeny: A New Word, A New World*, Penguin, 1984...3
76. Roberts, Jane. *The After Death Journal of an American Philosopher*, Prentice Hall, 1979...132
77. Ruse, Michael, in Reference 59...25
78. Russell, Bertrand. *A Free Man's Worship*, in *Mysticism & Logic*, Allen & Unwin, 1963...4
79. Russell, E. W. *Design for Destiny*, Neville Spearman, 1973...134
80. *Scientific & Medical Network Newsletter* No. 37, 1988...63
81. Sheldrake, Rupert. *A New Science of Life*, Miller Blond & Briggs, 1981...100, 104, 145
82. Silk, J. *The Big Bang*, 1981, USA, W. H. Freeman, 1989...84
83. Simpson, G. G. *The Meaning of Evolution*, Mentor, USA, 1949/55...115
84. Smith, Lester, ed. *Intelligence Came First*, TPH, 1975...98
85. Smith, Maynard. *The Meaning of Evolution*, Pelican, 1977...113
86. Smith and Williams. *Basic Human Embryology*, Pitman, 1966/84...47
87. Standen, Anthony. *The Human Spirit*, ed W. Burnett, Allen & Unwin, 1960...56, 142
88. Talbot, Michael. *Mysticism & the New Physics*, RKP, 1981...100
89. Taylor, G. R. *The Great Evolution Mystery*, Secker & Warburg, 1983...57, 61, 63, 121, 150
90. Thomas, Lowell. *Seven Wonders of the World*, Warburg Muller, 1957...45
91. *Trends in Ecology and Evolution*, Vol. 2, No. 3, Mar. 1987...37
92. Unpublished Correspondence...40, 53, 103, 119
93. Walker, E. H. *The Nature of Consciousness*, in 'Mathematical Bioscience', 1970...7, 19, 101

94. Watson, Lyall. *Lifetide*, Hodder, 1979...45, 102
95. Watson, David. *The Great Brain Robbery*, David Walker, 1975/89...7, 74
96. Weatherhead, Leslie. *The Christian Agnostic*, Hodder, 1965...128
97. Wilber, Ken. *Quantum Questions*, Shambala, 1984 (also Heisenberg et al. Ref. 36)...23
98. Wysong. *The Creation-Evolution Controversy*, 1987 (Obtainable from Inquiry Press, 1880 North Eastman, Midland, Michigan 48640, USA)...91

Late additions:

99. Ambrose, E. J. *The Mirror of Creation*, Scottish Academic Press...121
100. Ash & Hewett. *Science of the Gods*, Arkana, 1990...155
101. Davies, Paul. *Superforce*, Heinemann, 1984...159
102. Fix, Wm. R. *The Bone Peddlers*, Macmillan Pub. Co., New York...93
103. Gould, S. J. *Wonderful Life*, Penguin 1991...161
104. Lewin, Roger. *The Bones of Contention*, Penguin, 1989...94
105. Wesson, Robert. *Beyond Natural Selection*, MIT Press, New York, 1991...4, 48, 93

INDEX